Electronics for Experimenters

By the same author

Basic Quantum Chemistry

Electronics
for Experimenters
in Chemistry
Physics and Biology

Leon F. Phillips
Department of Chemistry, University of Canterbury

John Wiley & Sons, Inc., New York · London · Sydney

For Linda or Timothy

Preface

A working knowledge of electronics has long been regarded as essential equipment for a physicist or an electrical engineer. For graduates in other fields, however, such knowledge has often been considered an unnecessary luxury. This position has altered somewhat in recent years, first because of the massive takeover of chemistry and the current invasion of biology by such electronically oriented techniques as nuclear magnetic resonance, infrared spectroscopy, electron microscopy, and mass spectrometry, and second because of the development of undergraduate courses in which a high degree of specialization in one subject is balanced by less intensive forays into peripheral fields like electronics. With the greater concentration of electronic equipment in research laboratories there is usually an increase in the amount of technical assistance available to help keep the instruments in service, but this assistance certainly does not justify the research worker's remaining ignorant of what goes on inside the black boxes.

The aim of this book is to provide a more or less pocket-sized account of the parts of electronics that are of particular use to experimenters in chemistry, physics, and biology. It should serve either as a text for a formal lecture or laboratory course, or as primary reading material for a course of self-study. The treatment is kept as straightforward as possible, with emphasis on function rather than physics, and the usual basic physics course offered to undergraduates majoring in chemistry should be ample preparation. Perhaps it is not quite a law of nature, but the most important experiments generally seem to involve the most elusive signals, and with this in mind a great deal of attention is given to the noise and frequency limitations of amplifiers, to the problem of separating signals from noise, and to the techniques for handling small pulses. Many of the factors involved appear to advantage in instruments for measuring low light intensities, and several instruments for this purpose are described in some detail.

The idea I have attempted to convey throughout the book is that these are circuits which anyone can design. For this reason actual component values have been specified in as many of the circuits as possible. These circuits, or ones so like them that the difference is immaterial, have been built and do work. It must be pointed out, however, that no account has been taken of production spreads in the characteristics of components, and in individual cases it may be necessary to alter some component values in order to obtain the anticipated performance from the circuit. No doubt some of the circuits may be of direct practical use to the reader.

One feature of this book that will not please everyone is the simplified treatment of transistor parameters. There is no question about the general superiority of the hybrid parameters (which are here relegated to an appendix!), but in my view the use of the parameters α and β is more instructive for a beginner and is normally adequate in practice, even for an expert.

It is a pleasure to acknowledge the contributions of a number of persons to this book, especially Mr. G. G. Yates, formerly of the Department of Physical Chemistry, University of Cambridge, whose lectures to chemistry graduate students were greatly appreciated and who designed the circuits for the chopper photometer described in Chapter 10. Thanks are also due to Mr. T. I. Quickenden for the block diagram of his photon counter, to Drs. W. S. Metcalf and T. J. Seed for helpful discussions of other circuits, and to various manufacturers, all of whom are cited in the text, for providing data about their products. Finally, grateful thanks must be expressed to Miss Denise Russell who patiently typed a difficult manuscript.

LEON F. PHILLIPS

Christchurch, New Zealand
November, 1965

Contents

Electronics for Experimenters

1

Simple Network Theory

....

1a INTRODUCTION

The components of an electronic circuit can be classified as either active or passive, according to their response to an incoming electrical signal. Thus vacuum tubes and transistors are generally regarded as active components, and resistors, capacitors, and inductors are considered to be passive. The essential distinction is that in a network composed entirely of passive components the input and output voltages and currents are always linearly related to one another. If active components are present the dependence is generally more complex, as will be seen later. In this chapter we shall consider the behavior of passive components, both individually and in combination to form networks. These components normally play a subsidiary role in a circuit, their duties being to convey signals from one part of the circuit to another, to filter out unwanted signals, and to provide a congenial environment in which the active components can go about their work.

We shall need to consider the behavior of resistors, capacitors, and inductors with respect to both alternating and direct current (ac and dc), because when a number of components are linked together it is their behavior towards direct current which governs the quiescent properties of the resulting circuit, whereas their behavior towards alternating current governs the reception which is given to an incoming signal. In the next section we shall consider resistance, capacitance, and inductance individually. Following this we shall discuss some simple networks, namely the series and parallel *LC* resonant

1

circuits, the *RC* integrating network, and the *RC* differentiating network. In the final section of this chapter we shall describe the useful twin-T network.

1b RESISTANCE, CAPACITANCE, AND INDUCTANCE

Resistance, as is well known, obeys Ohm's law, and the materials of which resistors are constructed are invariably chosen so as not to upset this belief. The resistance *R*, expressed in ohms (Ω), is the same for both alternating current and direct current, except that at very high frequencies the current tends to travel over the surface of a conductor rather than through the interior, and the effective resistance increases. At high frequencies the effects of "stray" capacitance and inductance are also likely to become apparent. When stray capacitance and inductance can be neglected, the ac current through a resistor is in phase with the applied ac voltage.

The unit of capacitance is the farad (F), which is the capacitance of a body whose potential is increased by one volt by the addition of one coulomb of electric charge. Practical capacitors (also called "condensers") have capacitances which are conveniently expressed either in microfarads (μF) or in picofarads ($\mu\mu$F, or pF, pronounced "puffs"). A capacitor presents an essentially infinite resistance to direct current, but a finite *reactance* to alternating current. If the capacitance is *C* farads the reactance is $1/\omega C$ ohms, where $\omega = 2\pi f$ is the circular frequency of the alternating current. The term "reactance" is used when the current and the applied voltage are 90° out of phase. For capacitance the current *leads* the applied voltage by 90°. (Cf. Exercise 1.1.)

The unit of inductance is the henry (H), which is the inductance of a conductor such that an electromotive force of one volt is induced when the current through the conductor is changed at the rate of one ampere per second. (The direction of the induced current is always such as to oppose the change which causes it.) If the primary current and the induced emf are in different circuits, this is referred to as "mutual inductance," while if the primary current and the induced emf are in the same circuit, this is referred to as "self-inductance." We are mainly interested in self-inductance, which is a property of any conductor and does not depend on another circuit being nearby, although the applications of mutual inductance to transformers are obviously of great importance in engineering. An inductor generally possesses a low resistance to direct current and a relatively high reactance to alternating current. The reactance of a pure inductance of L henries is ωL ohms, and the current lags 90° *behind* the applied voltage (Exercise 1.1).

The essential features of the behavior of R, C, and L towards alternating current are summarized in Fig. 1.1. When designing a circuit that is to include reactance, it is usual to prefer capacitance to inductance, if the application is one for which either would do, because capacitance is both cheaper and relatively easy to obtain in any particular value. To obtain a particular value of inductance it may be necessary to have a coil especially wound.

In a practical circuit there will be more than one of the three elements R, C, and L, and it is therefore necessary to be able to

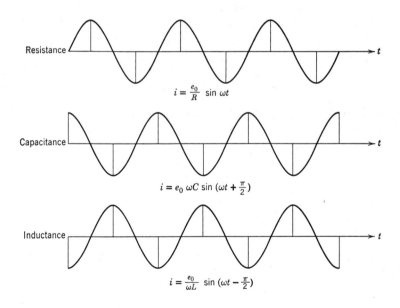

$$i = \frac{e_0}{R} \sin \omega t$$

$$i = e_0\, \omega C \sin \left(\omega t + \frac{\pi}{2}\right)$$

$$i = \frac{e_0}{\omega L} \sin \left(\omega t - \frac{\pi}{2}\right)$$

Fig. 1.1　Relative phases of ac currents in resistive, capacitive, and inductive circuits.

calculate the ratio of current to applied voltage for such a combination. The dc case is straightforward and we shall concentrate on the situation with ac. Experimentally we would measure the applied voltage $\mathscr{E}$ with an ac voltmeter connected in parallel with the combination, and measure $\mathscr{I}$, the current flowing, with an ac ammeter in series with the combination. The ratio of these *measured* quantities gives the magnitude of the *impedance*, Z, in the form

$$\mathscr{E} = \mathscr{I} \cdot |Z| \tag{1.1}$$

This is obviously analogous to Ohm's law

$$E = IR \tag{1.2}$$

but with the difference that Z is really a vector quantity, being the resultant of a resistive component R and a reactive component $(\omega L - 1/\omega C)$ at right angles to one another. A convenient way of taking account of this is to use the real quantity R for resistance and the imaginary quantities $j\omega L$ and $1/j\omega C$ for the reactances. (Here it is customary to use j for $\sqrt{-1}$ instead of i in order to avoid confusion with the symbol for an electric current.)

We can now apply Ohm's law in the form

$$e = i(R + j\omega L - j/\omega C) \tag{1.3}$$

where the real part of the equation refers to the component of the current which is in phase with the applied voltage and the imaginary part refers to the component which is 90° out of phase with the applied voltage. If the imaginary part is positive this component lags behind the applied voltage, and if the imaginary part is negative this component leads.

The vector impedance is therefore given by

$$Z = R + j(\omega L - 1/\omega C) \tag{1.4}$$

and the absolute magnitude of Z in ohms is given by

$$|Z| = \sqrt{R^2 + (\omega L - 1/\omega C)^2} \tag{1.5}$$

It is this magnitude of Z which appears in equation (1.1).

When Z is expressed in the form (1.4) the usual expressions

$$Z = Z_1 + Z_2 + Z_3 + \cdots \tag{1.6}$$

and

$$\frac{1}{Z} = \frac{1}{Z_1} + \frac{1}{Z_2} + \frac{1}{Z_3} + \cdots \tag{1.7}$$

apply to impedances connected in series and in parallel, respectively. The reciprocal of impedance is given the name *admittance* and is expressed in ohm^{-1}. Complicated networks of resistance and reactance can be analyzed by making use of *Kirchhoff's laws* in the form

$$\sum i = 0 \tag{1.8}$$

for steady currents entering and leaving a point, and

$$\sum Zi = e \tag{1.9}$$

for the total ac voltage drop around a closed circuit in a steady-current network containing a source of ac voltage of magnitude e.

1c RESONANT CIRCUITS

Suppose that we have inductance and capacitance in series in a circuit, as in Fig. 1.2, where r represents the residual resistance of the induction coil and connecting wires. For this circuit equation (1.6) is identical with equation (1.4), and the current and voltage are therefore related simply by (1.3). If the frequency of the applied voltage is allowed to vary, we note that the impedance passes through a minimum at $\omega L = 1/\omega C$, and that when this happens the current and the applied voltage are in phase with one another. This is an example of *resonance*. The value of ω (or f) given by $\omega = (LC)^{-\frac{1}{2}}$ is termed the resonant frequency of the circuit. If the applied voltage

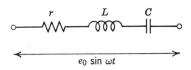

$e_0 \sin \omega t$

Fig. 1.2   Series resonant circuit.

is kept constant the resonance curve (Fig. 1.3) may be traced out by varying either ω or one of the reactances, L or C.   It is usually most convenient to vary C in order to tune the circuit to resonance.

At resonance the voltage across the whole circuit is equal to ir, but the voltage across either the coil or the condenser separately is $i\omega L$. It is possible for the second voltage to be very much greater than the first, and the ratio of these two voltages is known as the Q factor of the resonant circuit, i.e.,

$$Q = \omega L/r \qquad (1.10)$$

As indicated in Fig. 1.3, a higher value of Q corresponds to a sharper peak in the frequency response of the circuit.   Thus, for a fairly typical coil, resonating at a frequency of 5 megacycles with a resistance of 100 ohms and an inductance of 1.0 millihenry, we would have

$$Q = \frac{2\pi \times 5 \times 10^6 \times 1.0 \times 10^{-3}}{100} = 314$$

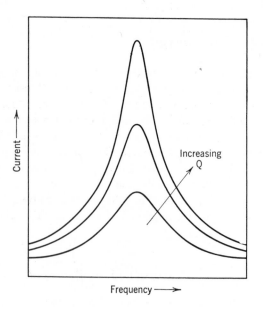

Fig. 1.3   Resonance curves for capacitance and inductance in series.

The quantity Q is widely used as a figure of merit for tuned circuits and resonant cavities which are designed to respond to small signals at radio or microwave frequencies. The definition used for resonant cavities, for which r and L are obviously rather difficult to define, is

$$Q = \frac{\omega \times \text{energy stored per cycle}}{\text{energy dissipated per cycle}} \qquad (1.11)$$

It can be shown that this is equivalent to the definition (1.10) for the Q of a resonant coil (cf., Exercise 1.2). A further definition, which enables Q to be determined from the shape of the resonance peak, is

$$Q = \frac{f_0}{\text{bandwidth}} \qquad (1.12)$$

Here f_0 is the resonant frequency ($= \omega_0/2\pi$) and the bandwidth is the width of the resonance peak, in cycles per second, between the half-power points. Since the power which is dissipated in the circuit is $\mathscr{I}^2 r$, the half-power points are the two frequencies for which $\mathscr{I}_0 = \sqrt{2}\,\mathscr{I}$.

A resonant circuit in the configuration of Fig. 1.4, with L and C in parallel, can be maintained in oscillation by a repetitive signal which has a small component at the resonant frequency, $\omega = (LC)^{-\frac{1}{2}}$. This type of LC network is often termed a "tank circuit."

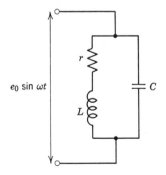

Fig. 1.4 Parallel resonant circuit.

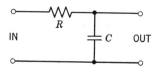

Fig. 1.5   Integrating network.

1d   SIMPLE *RC* NETWORKS

Integrating Network. Consider the circuit diagram of Fig. 1.5. This represents a four-terminal network, with two input terminals and two output terminals.   To begin with, we suppose that a high-impedance dc voltmeter is connected across the output terminals, and we consider the effect of suddenly applying a voltage step of height V_o across the input terminals (Fig. 1.6a).   The capacitor is charged by the current which flows through the resistance R, and the voltage across the capacitor at a time t after the application of the voltage step is given[1] by

$$V = V_o(1 - e^{-t/RC}) \qquad (1.13)$$

The variation of the output voltage with time (the "output waveform") is as shown in Fig. 1.6b.   We note that when t is small, compared with RC, the voltage rise at the output is linear, being given by

$$V = V_o t/RC \qquad (1.14)$$

The quantity RC is known as the *time constant* of the network.

If, after a further time T, the voltage step is suddenly removed from the input terminals (and these terminals are short-circuited), the capacitor discharges through R and the output voltage falls according to

$$V = V_o e^{-t/RC} \qquad (1.15)$$

The complete input square wave and output waveform are now as shown in Figs. 1.6c and 1.6d.

If RC is very large compared with T, the duration of the input pulse,

---

[1] To obtain this result, solve the equation $dV/dt = i/C = (V_o - V)/RC$ with the boundary condition $V = 0$ at $t = 0$.

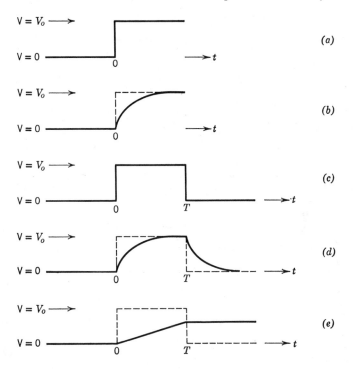

Fig. 1.6   Waveforms in an integrating network.

the output voltage rises linearly to a value V_oT/RC and then falls very slowly after the voltage step has been removed.   This is shown in Fig. 1.6e.   In this case the final output voltage is proportional to the area under the input waveform of Fig. 1.6c and the input waveform is said to have been integrated.   Since a waveform of any shape can be regarded as the sum of a series of rectangular pulses, it follows that any input signal will be integrated if its duration is much less than the time constant of the network.   This is often an undesirable effect and care must be taken to avoid it—for example, by keeping input and output impedances low and eliminating stray capacitance, in work involving high-frequency signals or very short pulses.

Next we consider the response of the integrating network to an orthodox ac voltage, $e_0 \sin \omega t$.   To make our derivation as useful

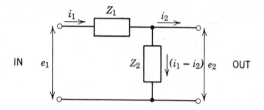

Fig. 1.7   Network with generalized impedances.

as possible we consider the circuit with general impedances Z as in Fig. 1.7.   Here we have, by Kirchhoff's laws,

$$e_1 = i_1 Z_1 + (i_1 - i_2)Z_2$$

and
$$e_2 = (i_1 - i_2)Z_2$$

Solving for e_1 and i_1 gives

$$e_1 = (Z_1 + Z_2)e_2/Z_2 + Z_1 i_2 \qquad (1.16)$$

and
$$i_1 = e_2/Z_2 + i_2 \qquad (1.17)$$

We can use matrix notation to combine these two equations into one, in the form

$$\begin{pmatrix} e_1 \\ i_1 \end{pmatrix} = \begin{pmatrix} (Z_1 + Z_2)/Z_2 & Z_1 \\ 1/Z_2 & 1 \end{pmatrix} \times \begin{pmatrix} e_2 \\ i_2 \end{pmatrix} \qquad (1.18)$$

The main virtue of using this notation is that if two networks are cascaded, as in Fig. 1.8, we have

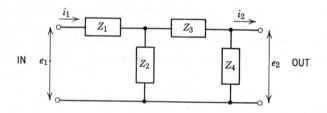

Fig. 1.8   Cascaded networks.

$$\begin{pmatrix} e_1 \\ i_1 \end{pmatrix} = \begin{pmatrix} (Z_1 + Z_2)/Z_2 & Z_1 \\ 1/Z_2 & 1 \end{pmatrix} \begin{pmatrix} (Z_3 + Z_4)/Z_4 & Z_3 \\ 1/Z_4 & 1 \end{pmatrix} \begin{pmatrix} e_2 \\ i_2 \end{pmatrix} \quad (1.19)$$

where the matrix multiplication rule[2] enables the equations for transforming e_2 and i_2 into e_1 and i_1 to be written out directly. This notation can obviously be extended to deal with any number of networks in series.

For our single integrating network we have $Z_1 = R$ and $Z_2 = -j/\omega C$. Equation 1.18 therefore becomes

$$\begin{pmatrix} e_1 \\ i_1 \end{pmatrix} = \begin{pmatrix} 1 + j\omega CR & R \\ j\omega C & 1 \end{pmatrix} \begin{pmatrix} e_2 \\ i_2 \end{pmatrix} \quad (1.20)$$

In many applications the output of the network is terminated by a high impedance, e.g., the grid circuit of a vacuum tube. If we suppose this to be so, we can put $i_2 = 0$ and obtain

$$e_1 = e_2(1 + j\omega CR) \quad (1.21)$$

or in terms of measured voltages

$$\mathscr{E}_1 = \mathscr{E}_2(1 + \omega^2 C^2 R^2)^{\frac{1}{2}} \quad (1.22)$$

Differentiating Network. A diagram of this network is given in Fig. 1.9. Again we begin by considering the effect of applying a voltage step across the input, with a high-impedance dc voltmeter connected across the output. There is no need to go through the

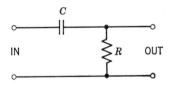

Fig. 1.9 Differentiating network.

---

[2] The matrix multiplication rule is included in a summary of elementary matrix algebra given in Appendix 1.

process of solving the differential equation for the voltage across the resistor, since this is equal to the input voltage less the voltage across the capacitor, and the voltage across the capacitor must be the same as we have just calculated for the integrating network.   Hence

$$V = V_o e^{-t/RC} \tag{1.23}$$

at the beginning, and

$$V = -V_o e^{-t/RC} \tag{1.24}$$

at the end.   The corresponding input and output waveforms are shown in Fig. 1.10.

If the time constant RC is very much less than T, the duration of the input pulse, the output approximates the result that would be obtained by mathematical differentiation of the input pulse.   This effect is often undesirable, and can be reduced by making the time constant of the network as large as possible.

When a continuous ac voltage is applied to the input terminals, the input and output currents and voltages are related by equation (1.18), with $Z_1 = -j/\omega C$ and $Z_2 = R$.   The result is

$$\begin{pmatrix} e_1 \\ i_1 \end{pmatrix} = \begin{pmatrix} 1 - j/\omega CR & -j/\omega C \\ 1/R & 1 \end{pmatrix} \begin{pmatrix} e_2 \\ i_2 \end{pmatrix} \tag{1.25}$$

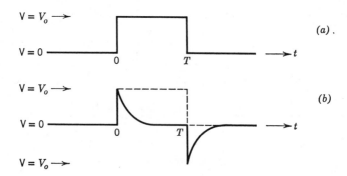

Fig. 1.10   Input and output waveforms for a differentiating network.

As before, if the output of the network operates into a high impedance we can assume $i_2 = 0$ and obtain

$$e_1 = e_2(1 - j/\omega CR) \tag{1.26}$$

and in terms of measured voltages

$$\mathscr{E}_1 = \mathscr{E}_2(1 + 1/\omega^2 C^2 R^2)^{\frac{1}{2}} \tag{1.27}$$

1e THE TWIN-T NETWORK

Consider the T network shown in Fig. 1.11. By making use of Kirchhoff's laws we can obtain expressions for i_1 and i_2 in the form

$$\begin{pmatrix} i_1 \\ i_2 \end{pmatrix} = (A) \begin{pmatrix} e_1 \\ e_2 \end{pmatrix} \tag{1.28}$$

where (A) is the matrix

$$\begin{pmatrix} a_{11} & a_{12} \\ a_{21} & a_{22} \end{pmatrix}$$

and the elements a_{mn} depend on the various impedances in the network. The nature of this dependence does not concern us immediately.

Now if a second network is connected in parallel with the first the two networks will have the same input and output voltages. Thus for the second network

$$\begin{pmatrix} i_1' \\ i_2' \end{pmatrix} = (A') \begin{pmatrix} e_1 \\ e_2 \end{pmatrix} \tag{1.29}$$

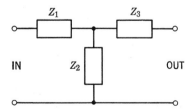

Fig. 1.11 T network.

So for the two networks together

$$\begin{pmatrix} i_1 + i_1' \\ i_2 + i_2' \end{pmatrix} = (A'')\begin{pmatrix} e_1 \\ e_2 \end{pmatrix} \tag{1.30}$$

where $(A'') = (A + A') = \begin{pmatrix} a_{11} + a_{11}' & a_{12} + a_{12}' \\ a_{21} + a_{21}' & a_{22} + a_{22}' \end{pmatrix}$ (1.31)

in accordance with the rule for matrix addition (Appendix 1).   This gives us a general method of making calculations for networks in parallel.

For the network of Fig. 1.11 we have

$$(Z_1 + Z_2)i_1 - Z_2 i_2 - e_1 = 0 \tag{1.32}$$

and $$Z_2 i_1 - (Z_2 + Z_3)i_2 - e_2 = 0 \tag{1.33}$$

which can be solved for i_1 and i_2 in the normal way.   The result is

$$i_1 = (Z_1 Z_2 + Z_2 Z_3 + Z_3 Z_1)^{-1}([Z_2 + Z_3]e_1 - Z_2 e_2) \tag{1.34}$$
$$i_2 = (Z_1 Z_2 + Z_2 Z_3 + Z_3 Z_1)^{-1}(Z_2 e_1 - [Z_1 + Z_2]e_2) \tag{1.35}$$

or, in matrix form,

$$\begin{pmatrix} i_1 \\ i_2 \end{pmatrix} = \begin{pmatrix} \dfrac{Z_2 + Z_3}{Z} & -\dfrac{Z_2}{Z} \\[2mm] \dfrac{Z_2}{Z} & -\dfrac{Z_1 + Z_2}{Z} \end{pmatrix}\begin{pmatrix} e_1 \\ e_2 \end{pmatrix} \tag{1.36}$$

where Z stands for $Z_1 Z_2 + Z_2 Z_3 + Z_3 Z_1$.   With two such networks in parallel we have

$$\begin{pmatrix} i_1 + i_1' \\ i_2 + i_2' \end{pmatrix} = \begin{pmatrix} \left(\dfrac{Z_2 + Z_3}{Z} + \dfrac{S_2 + S_3}{S}\right) & -\left(\dfrac{Z_2}{Z} + \dfrac{S_2}{S}\right) \\[2mm] \left(\dfrac{Z_2}{Z} + \dfrac{S_2}{S}\right) & -\left(\dfrac{Z_1 + Z_2}{Z} + \dfrac{S_1 + S_2}{S}\right) \end{pmatrix}\begin{pmatrix} e_1 \\ e_2 \end{pmatrix} \tag{1.37}$$

where we have used S instead of Z for the impedances in the second network.

The practical importance of the twin-T network arises from the fact that it can be constructed to provide infinite attenuation for alternating current of one particular frequency. This property is often exploited in circuits designed to respond to one frequency alone. (Some examples of how this can be achieved are described in Chapter 7.)

To find the condition for infinite attenuation we suppose that the output of the network is working into a high impedance, so that $(i_2 + i_2')$ is effectively equal to zero. From (1.37) we have then

$$e_1\left(\frac{Z_2}{Z} + \frac{S_2}{S}\right) = e_2\left(\frac{Z_1 + Z_2}{Z} + \frac{S_1 + S_2}{S}\right) \qquad (1.38)$$

so that if the attenuation of e_1 by the network is infinite, i.e., if e_2 is zero, we must have

$$\frac{Z_2}{Z} + \frac{S_2}{S} = 0 \qquad (1.39)$$

In its usual form (Fig. 1.12) the twin-T network has $Z_1 = Z_3 = R$, $Z_2 = -j/2\omega C$, $S_1 = S_3 = -j/\omega C$, and $S_2 = R/2$. Hence

$$Z = \frac{R^2 - Rj}{\omega C} = \frac{R(1 + j\omega CR)}{j\omega C} \qquad (1.40)$$

and

$$S = -\frac{1}{\omega^2 C^2} - \frac{Rj}{\omega C} = -\frac{1 + j\omega CR}{\omega^2 C^2} \qquad (1.41)$$

and equation (1.39) becomes

$$0 = \frac{1/2R - R\omega^2 C^2/2}{1 + j\omega CR}$$

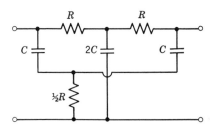

Fig. 1.12 Twin-T network.

This immediately gives the condition

$$R\omega C = 1 \qquad (1.42)$$

or, in terms of frequency f in cycles per second,

$$f = 1/2\pi RC \qquad (1.43)$$

The result (1.43) enables a network to be designed to possess infinite attenuation at any desired frequency.

EXERCISES

1.1   The voltages across a capacitance C and an inductance L are given by $V = qC$ and $V = -L\,di/dt$, respectively, where $i = dq/dt$ is the current flowing at any instant.   Show that if the voltage is of the form $V_0 \sin \omega t$, the currents are given by $V_0 \omega C \sin (\omega t + \pi/2)$ and $(V_0/\omega L) \sin (\omega t - \pi/2)$, respectively.

1.2   Verify that the energy stored in an inductance is $\frac{1}{2}Li^2$, whereas that stored in a capacitance is $\frac{1}{2}qV = \frac{1}{2}CV^2$.   Here V is the instantaneous value of the voltage across the capacitor.   The energy dissipated by the residual resistance of an inductor is i^2r per unit time.   Hence show that for the resonant circuits of Figs. 1.2 and 1.4 the two definitions of Q, equations (1.10) and (1.11), are equivalent.

1.3   Consider the network below.   Show that for $R_1 R_2 = 1/\omega^2 C_1 C_2$ the input and output are in phase, and that for $R_1 = R_2 = R$, $C_1 = C_2 = C$ the output voltage is one-third of the input voltage when they are in phase.   (It is necessary to assume that $i_2 = 0$.)   What happens if the output of this network is fed back to the input via an amplifier of zero phase shift and gain greater than or equal to 3 ?

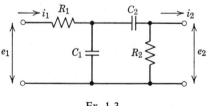

Ex. 1-3

1.4 Derive an expression for the impedance of the parallel resonant circuit of Fig. 1.4. [Rationalize the denominator in the expression which is obtained by applying equation (1.7).] What is the condition that this impedance should be purely resistive? Show that for the coil which is described in section 1c the error in assuming $\omega = (LC)^{-\frac{1}{2}}$ at resonance is very small.

REFERENCES

1. D. Owen, *Alternating current measurements*. London: Methuen & Co., Third Edition, 1950, pp. 1–21.
2. F. J. M. Farley, *Elements of pulse circuits*. London: Methuen & Co., 1955, pp. 1–16.
3. R. E. Scott, *Linear circuits, Part 1. Time domain analysis; Part 2. Frequency domain analysis.* London: Addison-Wesley, 1960.

2

The Properties of Vacuum Tubes

....

2a INTRODUCTION

A thermionic vacuum tube consists of an evacuated envelope, usually of glass, into which are inserted two or more electrodes. One of the electrodes serves as the cathode and another as the anode (also called the "plate"). The remaining electrodes, if any, take the form of wire grids which occupy the space between anode and cathode. The most common arrangement has cylindrical symmetry, with the cathode at the center and the anode on the outside (Fig. 2.1). The residual gas pressure in the tube is 10^{-5} torr or less.

Tubes are classified as diodes, triodes, tetrodes, pentodes, hexodes, or heptodes according to whether they possess 2, 3, 4, 5, 6, or 7 electrodes. It is common practice for two tubes to be contained in the same envelope, typical combinations being diode-triode, triode-triode, and triode-hexode.

When a tube is in operation the cathode is heated electrically to a temperature at which it emits electrons, this process being known as thermionic emission. The cathode may be in the form of a metal strip through which the heater current passes directly, or it may be in the form of a cylinder which is indirectly heated by an enclosed filament. The electron-emitting surface can be pure tungsten, thoriated tungsten (tungsten coated with thorium oxide), or nickel alloy coated with alkaline-earth oxides. The electrons emitted by the cathode are attracted towards the anode, the number that actually arrive there being dependent on the anode potential and on the potentials of any intervening grids.

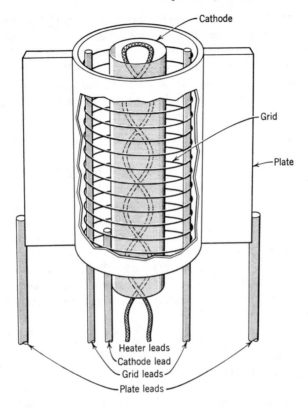

Fig. 2.1 Internal construction of a triode vacuum tube.

The great usefulness of vacuum tubes depends on the following three basic properties.

1. The current through the tube can flow in one direction only, i.e., from anode to cathode in terms of the *conventional positive current*, or from cathode to anode in terms of the flow of electrons. This opens the way to a number of applications which depend on turning alternating current into direct current.

2. The current through the tube can be made to follow the fluctuating potential of one or more of the grids. This makes it possible to amplify small voltages which are applied to a grid (or small currents which can be made to develop corresponding voltages

at the grid) and to mix signals together by applying the signal voltages to different grids in the same tube.

3. If a sufficiently large negative potential is applied to a grid, the flow of electrons to the anode can be cut off completely. This means that a tube can operate as a switch, and since the transit time for electrons between cathode and anode can be as short as 10^{-9} sec, repetitive switching operations can be carried out at very high speed.

In many applications of electronics, work that was formerly done by vacuum tubes has now been taken over by transistors and other solid-state, semiconductor devices. There remains, however, a large number of applications in which vacuum tubes are used in preference to these devices. This preference is partly the result of inertia, since transistors have been in large-scale production for only a comparatively short time, but it is also true that in many situations vacuum tubes can give superior performance. The relative merits of vacuum tubes and their solid-state counterparts will be discussed at the end of the next chapter. The rest of the present chapter will consist of descriptions of the characteristics of most of the important types of tubes.

2b THE VACUUM DIODE

Diodes are designed to capitalize on the fact that electrons can flow only from cathode to anode and will not flow in the reverse direction when the voltage supply is reversed. This enables a diode to convert alternating current into direct current, the conversion process usually being termed *rectification* if moderate or large amounts of power are involved and *detection* if only small amounts are involved. Vacuum diodes are commonly used as rectifiers in dc power supplies designed to operate from ac mains, and as detectors in radio receivers when a modulated high-frequency ac signal is to be converted into a similarly modulated dc signal. If very large amounts of power or high voltages are to be rectified, vacuum diodes give way to gas-filled rectifiers, as will be explained shortly. Some typical circuits that can be used with rectifiers and detectors will be described in Chapter 6.

The symbol used in circuit diagrams to represent a vacuum diode

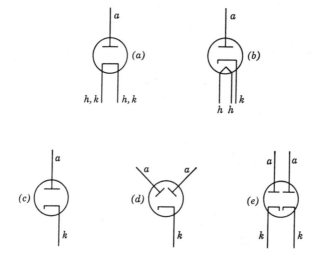

Fig. 2.2 Circuit symbols for diodes: a = anode, k = cathode, h = heater.

with a directly heated cathode is shown in Fig. 2.2a, and that for a diode with an indirectly heated cathode in Fig. 2.2b. We shall usually omit the heater connections from circuit diagrams, unless there is some special reason for putting them in, and show both of these diodes as in Fig. 2.2c. Two alternative ways of including two diodes in a single envelope are shown in Figs. 2.2d and 2.2e. In the first tube, which is meant to be used as a full-wave rectifier (see Chapter 6), the two diodes have a common cathode. An example of this would be an RCA type 6X4, or Mullard EZ80. In the second tube the double diode has two separate cathodes, and the two halves of the tube function independently. An example would be RCA type 6AL5, or Mullard EB91.

A typical diode "characteristic" is shown in Fig. 2.3, where the anode current i_a is plotted against the anode voltage v_a. It is seen that the anode current is never negative and that it increases with increasing v_a, going from zero with v_a a few volts negative to a steady value, termed the "saturation current," when v_a is large and positive.[1]

---

[1] The characteristic shown is of the type that is observed with diodes having pure-tungsten cathodes. Diodes with oxide-coated cathodes usually show a "knee" in the characteristic rather than a true saturation current.

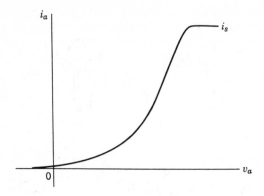

Fig. 2.3   Vacuum diode characteristic.

The explanation of the shape of the diode characteristic is as follows. Electrons are emitted from the cathode at a rate that depends only on its temperature and is independent of v_a. When v_a is low the cathode becomes surrounded by a cloud of evaporated electrons, the *space charge*, and these repel one another and also repel other electrons which are in the process of being emitted from the cathode. The only electrons that can reach the anode are those emitted with sufficient energy to overcome repulsion by the space

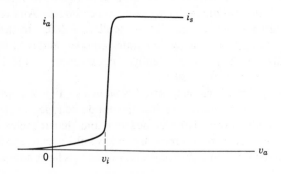

Fig. 2.4   Characteristic for a gas-filled diode.

charge.   In this condition the current is said to be space-charge-limited.   It was shown by Langmuir that when this is so the current in an infinite plane diode depends on $v_a^{3/2}$, and this result is also true for the usual cylindrical diodes when v_a is small.   As v_a is increased the amount of space charge decreases, and the current rises almost linearly until finally all the electrons that are emitted by the cathode are collected at the anode.   This is the saturation point, and further increase in v_a merely increases the energy with which the electrons arrive at the anode.   Most vacuum diodes, and especially those with oxide-coated cathodes, are rapidly destroyed by being operated in the saturation region; therefore it is never possible to make full use of all the cathode emission.

If a small amount (0.1 torr) of a gas, such as mercury vapor, is included in a diode the characteristic takes the form shown in Fig. 2.4, for the following reasons.   When the electron energy exceeds v_i, the ionization potential of the atoms in the vapor (typically about 20 V), positive ions are produced by electron bombardment of these atoms.   The positive ions are attracted into the space-charge region and neutralize the repulsion effects to such an extent that practically the whole of the cathode emission is able to flow to the anode at a comparatively low value of v_a.   This can happen without the excessive heating produced by high-energy electrons striking the anode and, more important, without the destructive effects produced by energetic ions, formed from residual gas in the vacuum envelope, striking the cathode.

For the majority of laboratory applications sufficient current can be carried by ordinary vacuum diodes, but where high currents and voltages are required (from about 100 mA at 700 V upwards) it is preferable to employ mercury vapor rectifiers—for example, the widely used 866A.

2c   THE TRIODE

We have seen that in a diode the anode current is controlled by the amount of negative space charge which surrounds the cathode. In a triode (Fig. 2.5) this control is taken over by a grid whose potential can be altered independently of the anode voltage.   The

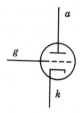

Fig. 2.5 Circuit symbol for a triode; a = anode, g = grid, k = cathode. (Heater connections not shown.)

triode plate characteristics of Fig. 2.6 are seen to be similar to the diode characteristic of Fig. 2.3, a different characteristic being obtained for each value of the grid potential.

A triode is normally operated with the grid a few volts negative with respect to the cathode.   If the grid is made positive with respect to the cathode, the grid-cathode system behaves as a diode and grid current flows.   This is usually undesirable.   If the grid potential is increased gradually from zero, the anode current remains stationary at first and then begins to fall as the grid current increases.

An alternative representation of the static characteristics of a triode is given in terms of the "mutual characteristics" of Fig. 2.7. Here the anode current is plotted as a function of grid potential at

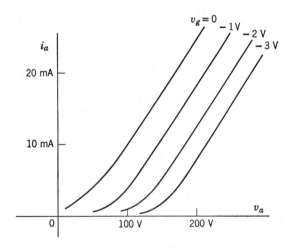

Fig. 2.6 Plate characteristics of a triode.

constant anode voltage. To show the characteristics of a triode
completely it would be necessary to construct a surface in three
dimensions, with v_a and v_g plotted along the x and y axes and i_a
along the z axis. The curves in Figs. 2.6 and 2.7 correspond to
different sections through this surface.

The static triode characteristics that we have considered so far
enable the operating point of a tube to be chosen from a number of
possible combinations of plate current and plate and grid potential.
They are also useful when we must obtain maximum efficiency from
a power amplifier or find conditions for operating the triode as an
ON/OFF switch. We shall consider these applications in detail later.

When dealing with the behavior of a triode as an amplifier of small
signals, it is convenient to make use of the *small-signal parameters*,
which are defined as follows. The anode current is a function of
the plate and grid potentials; i.e., we can write

$$i_a = i_a(v_a, v_g) \tag{2.1}$$

and so
$$di_a = \left(\frac{\partial i_a}{\partial v_a}\right)_{v_g} dv_a + \left(\frac{\partial i_a}{\partial v_g}\right)_{v_a} dv_g \tag{2.2}$$

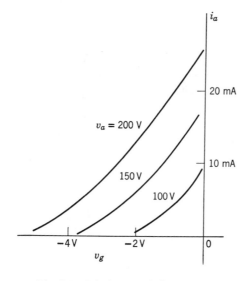

Fig. 2.7 Triode mutual characteristics.

If only small changes in the three quantities are involved, we can write

$$\delta i_a = \left(\frac{\partial i_a}{\partial v_a}\right)_{v_g} \delta v_a + \left(\frac{\partial i_a}{\partial v_g}\right)_{v_a} \delta v_g \tag{2.3}$$

(Sometimes the δ's are omitted from this equation and i_a, v_a, and v_g are understood to represent small changes in the parent quantities rather than the quantities themselves.)

The coefficient $(\partial i_a/\partial v_a)_{v_g}$ is normally written as $1/\rho$, where ρ is the *plate resistance* of the tube and is commonly equal to a few tens of thousands of ohms for a triode. The quantity $1/\rho$ is called the *anode conductance* and is sometimes given the symbol g_a.

The coefficient $(\partial i_a/\partial v_g)_{v_a}$ is known as the *mutual conductance*, or *transconductance*, and is given the symbol g_m. It is typically about 5×10^{-3} ohm^{-1}.

The quantity $-(\partial v_a/\partial v_g)_{i_a} = \mu$ is known as the *amplification factor*. If di_a is put equal to zero in equation (2.2), it is seen that

$$\mu = g_m \rho \tag{2.4}$$

With these definitions equation (2.2) can be rewritten as either

$$di_a = \frac{dv_a}{\rho} + g_m \, dv_g \tag{2.5}$$

or

$$\rho \, di_a = dv_a + \mu \, dv_g \tag{2.6}$$

Triodes are classified as high-mu, medium-mu, or low-mu, according to whether the amplification factor is greater than 50, between 10 and 50, or less than 10.

Triodes have many applications, and a great many different tubes have been designed to suit specific purposes. Typical applications are as voltage amplifiers (e.g., RCA 12AT7, Mullard ECC81), power amplifiers (RCA 2A3, Mullard 6080), and high-frequency oscillators (RCA 6AF4, Mullard ECC91).

Two main causes of dissatisfaction with the properties of triodes have led to efforts to improve on them and so to the design of multi-grid tubes. The first source of discontent, one that has been almost removed by the development of high-mu triodes, is the fact that the anode current depends markedly on the anode voltage. This limits the amount of gain that can be obtained from a triode amplifier

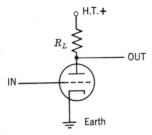

Fig. 2.8   Triode amplifier.

stage.   When a tube is used as a voltage amplifier the output voltage appears across a load resistor which is connected in series with the anode (Fig. 2.8).   If the anode current increases, as a result of an increase in grid potential, the voltage drop across the load resistor increases and the anode voltage correspondingly decreases.   This decrease in v_a produces a corresponding decrease in i_a, thus canceling out part of the effect of the original change in v_g.   Hence the gain of the amplifier is less than it would be if i_a were independent of v_a. The second, and more important, reason for seeking improvement is that the capacitance between grid and anode of a triode is quite appreciable (about 5 pF).   This leads to a direct interaction between grid and anode at high frequencies ("Miller effect"), resulting in a loss of gain at very high frequencies and a tendency for the amplifier to turn into an oscillator at moderately high frequencies.   These defects are largely overcome in the tubes considered in the next section.

2d   THE PENTODE (AND BEAM TETRODE)

The two aims of reducing the capacitance between control grid and anode and of screening the space charge around the cathode from the effect of variations in the anode voltage can be achieved simultaneously by introducing a positively charged screen grid between the control grid and the anode.   The result is a tetrode (Fig. 2.9).

The simple tetrode is much less successful than it ought to be because of a new effect which becomes important, namely the emission of secondary electrons from the anode.   The screen grid is

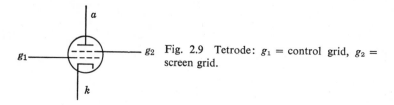

g_1

Fig. 2.9   Tetrode: g_1 = control grid, g_2 = screen grid.

normally held at a potential which is close to that of the anode when no signal is applied to the control grid.   Therefore the anode potential is likely to swing well below the screen potential when the control grid is made less negative by an incoming signal.   This swing would be harmless if it were not for the fact that electrons striking the anode bring about the emission of secondary electrons, which can be captured by the screen grid if they have the energy to travel far enough from the anode.   The resulting decrease in the anode current produces a large "kink" in the plate characteristic, as illustrated in Fig. 2.10.

The kink in the plate characteristic gives rise to distortion of the output of the tube and to instability of the circuit when the tube is operating in a region where $\partial i_a / \partial v_a$ is negative.   The size of the kink can be reduced considerably by concentrating the electron stream into a few compact beams in the region between screen and anode, so that the potential minimum (about 20 V) produced by the space charge in the beams repels most of the secondary electrons and

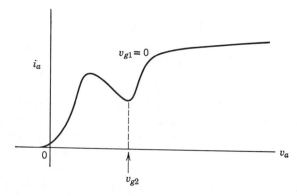

Fig. 2.10   Tetrode plate characteristic.

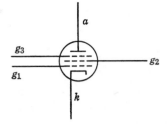

Fig. 2.11 Pentode: g_1 = control grid, g_2 = screen grid, g_3 = suppressor grid.

returns them to the anode. This is the method used in beam, or "kinkless," tetrodes.

A better method of overcoming secondary emission is to insert a third grid, known as a "suppressor," between screen grid and anode. The result is then a pentode (Fig. 2.11). The suppressor grid is usually connected directly to the cathode through the external circuit, and its large negative potential with respect to the anode is an effective barrier to secondary electrons. The suppressor grid is made to be of much coarser pitch than the others so that it does not interfere unduly with the primary electron stream.

The plate characteristics of a pentode are illustrated in Fig. 2.12. Each characteristic has a knee at about 20 V, and in the working region to the right of the knee the plate resistance $\rho = (\partial v_a/\partial i_a)_{v_g}$ is very large (typically 10^6 ohms). The amplification factor μ is not

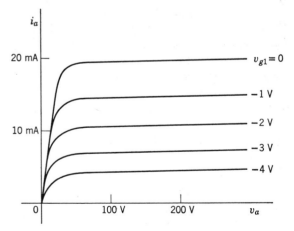

Fig. 2.12 Pentode plate characteristics: $v_{g2} = 200$ V, $v_{g3} = 0$.

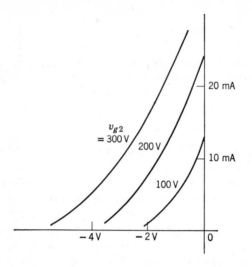

Fig. 2.13   Pentode mutual characteristics: $v_a =$
300 V.

usually specified for a pentode, the important quantity for deciding
the gain of an amplifier stage being the mutual conductance g_m.
It is easy to show that the voltage gain of a simple pentode amplifier
is $g_m R_L$, where R_L is the anode load (cf. Exercise 2.2). The mutual
conductance is typically 5×10^{-3} ohm^{-1}, so that with a load
resistor of 4×10^4 ohms (40 K) the gain is 200. This is about six
times the gain that would be obtained from a high-mu triode such as
the 12AX7 ($\mu = 100$) with the same anode load.

Pentode mutual characteristics (graphs of anode current versus
control grid voltage) are also given in tube manuals. A typical
example is shown in Fig. 2.13. Here the parameter which is used
to label each curve is the screen grid potential.

The amount of negative grid voltage required to reduce the anode
current to zero is termed the "grid base." Pentodes are classified
as remote cutoff, semiremote cutoff, and sharp cutoff, depending on
whether the control grid base is greater than 20%, between 10 and
20%, or less than 10% of the screen grid voltage. The applications
of pentodes are similar to those that have been mentioned for
triodes, but with the advantage that pentodes give better behavior
at high frequencies and usually have more available amplification.

2e OTHER TUBES

Hexodes, Heptodes, etc. It is sometimes desirable to be able to control the current through a tube by means of signals applied to two independent grids. The simplest way of going about this would be to inject the second signal through the suppressor grid of a pentode, but this method is not usually satisfactory because the wires of which the suppressor is composed are so widely spaced that the electron stream is relatively insensitive to variations in their potential. An indication of the degree of control exercised by a grid is the magnitude of the grid base. Thus for a typical sharp cutoff pentode —the 6AU6, for example—the anode current can be cut off completely by -6 V applied to grid 1, but it is necessary to apply about -90 V to grid 3 to produce the same effect.

A better approach to this problem is to use a tube with more than one control grid, i.e., a hexode or heptode. The hexode of Fig. 2.14 is essentially a tetrode to which an extra control grid g_3 and an extra screen grid g_4 have been added. The two screen grids, g_2 and g_4, are often connected internally. This sort of tube has the usual fault of tetrodes, namely a kink in the plate characteristics as a result of secondary emission from the anode.

The heptode of Fig. 2.15 is similar to the hexode just described, except that a suppressor grid g_5 has been added in order to remove the kink from the plate characteristics. Hexodes and heptodes are often included in the same envelope as a triode or pentode, sometimes with a common cathode, the second tube being intended to act as an amplifier or oscillator and having its output applied to one of the

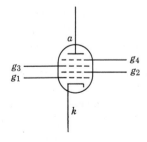

Fig. 2.14   Circuit symbol for a hexode.

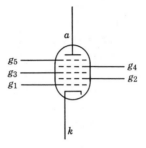

Fig. 2.15 Circuit symbol for a heptode.

control grids of the mixer tube. A typical example is provided by the input stage of an ordinary "superheterodyne" radio receiver, where an incoming radio-frequency signal is mixed with another signal that is generated within the receiver.

The Thyratron. If a small amount of gas (say, 0.1 torr) is introduced into a triode, the result is essentially a thyratron. The gas is commonly hydrogen, argon, or mercury. Such a tube behaves as an ordinary triode at low plate currents, but once the grid has been made sufficiently positive to start a moderate current flowing, the ionization builds up and a continuous discharge is formed. While the continuous discharge is running, the grid has no control over the current through the tube, and the discharge can only be turned off by reducing the anode voltage to less than the ionization potential of the gas. Currents of many amperes can be carried by thyratrons, with only small (about 20 V) potential differences between anode and cathode.

Typical applications of thyratrons are as relays, as controlled rectifiers of ac power, and as relaxation oscillators (cf. Chapter 9). The circuit symbol for a thyratron is given in Fig. 2.16.

Voltage Reference Tubes. Voltage reference tubes have the useful property that, at their proper working current, the voltage drop across the tube is almost independent of the amount of current flowing. This is a property of the cold-cathode discharge through a gas at low pressure.

The symbol which is used for a voltage reference tube and a

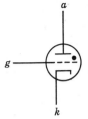

Fig. 2.16 Circuit symbol for a thyratron
(dot = gas-filled).

diagram of the electrode construction are given in Fig. 2.17. The
purpose of the short piece of wire shown pointing inwards from the
cylindrical cathode (Fig. 2.17*b*) is to reduce the amount of voltage
that must be applied to the tube in order to start the discharge.

   To see how such a tube behaves in practice we consider a particular
example, namely the 85A2. This tube supplies a reference voltage
which is nominally 85 V over the current range 1 to 10 mA, the
variation from tube to tube being ± 2 V. The *ignition voltage* which
is required to start the discharge is normally about 30 V greater than
the steady "burning" voltage. For the 85A2 the maximum ignition
voltage is stated to be 115 V in the presence of some ambient light;
in complete darkness the discharge may take some time to start even
at this voltage. Once the discharge is under way, the voltage across
the tube falls to the burning voltage, which is 83.3 V at 1 mA, and
rises to 86.2 V at 10 mA for a tube whose burning voltage is 85 V
at the *preferred current* of 6 mA. The burning voltage is very
reproducible, especially when the tube has been operated for a few
hundred hours. The typical drift of the voltage is 0.2% per 100
hours, or less than 0.01% in 8 hours after an initial 3-minute warm-up
period.

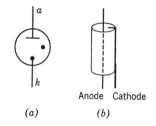

Anode Cathode

(a)   (b)

Fig. 2.17 Voltage reference tube: (*a*) circuit
symbol, (*b*) electrode construction.

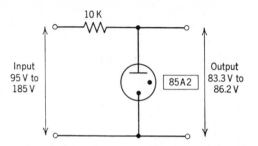

Fig. 2.18   Reference voltage circuit.

A circuit for obtaining a steady reference voltage is shown in Fig. 2.18. When the input voltage varies from 93 to 186 V, the current varies from 1 to 10 mA, and so the reference voltage varies from 83.3 to 86.2 V.   This type of circuit is useful when it is necessary to provide a constant voltage under conditions of almost constant current drain.   Regulated power supplies are usually required to provide a steady voltage independently of the amount of current being drawn over quite a large range, and this involves more elaborate circuitry, as described in Chapter 7.

Voltage reference tubes are not usually connected in parallel because of the difficulty of ensuring that the same current passes through each tube, but they are often connected in series in order to obtain higher voltages.   When they are connected in series it is advisable to insert bypass resistors, each of about 200 K, in order to reduce the amount of voltage required to ignite the tubes (Fig. 2.19). With this arrangement the tubes ignite one by one, starting from the bottom of the chain, and the excess ignition voltage is required for the top tube only.

Voltage reference tubes of the glow discharge type are available to provide stable voltages in the range from about 50 to 150 V, with preferred burning currents between 5 and 25 mA.   For high voltages, from about 300 V to 30 kV, voltage reference tubes are available which employ a corona discharge rather than a glow discharge.   An example is the Victoreen "Corotron."   These tubes have no "striking voltage" requirement, but their application is limited by electrical noise at very low burning currents.   The preferred operating current is typically one or two orders of magnitude smaller than the preferred current of an ordinary glow discharge tube.

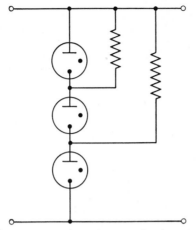

Fig. 2.19   Voltage reference tubes in series.

EXERCISES

2.1   Draw voltage-time curves for the outputs of the power rectifier circuits *a*, *b*, and *c*.   What happens to these curves if a capacitance C is connected in parallel with the load?

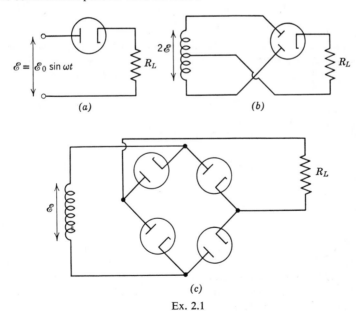

Ex. 2.1

2.2   From the equation

$$di_a = \frac{dv_a}{\rho} + g_m \, dv_g$$

show that for the circuit

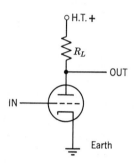

Ex. 2.2

the voltage gain is given by

$$\frac{dv_a}{dv_g} = -\frac{\mu R_L}{R_L + \rho}$$

where $\mu = g_m \rho$.   What happens to this result when ρ is very large, as is the case with a pentode?

2.3

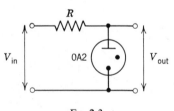

Ex. 2.3

The OA2 provides a 150-V reference voltage for the range of currents 5 to 30 mA.   If the input voltage in this circuit varies between 190 and 390 V, what should be the value of R?   The preferred burning current of the OA2 is 18 mA.   What should be the value of R if the input varies only between 190 and 240 V?

REFERENCES

1. W. H. Aldous and E. Appleton, *Thermionic vacuum tubes*. London: Methuen & Co., Sixth Edition, 1952, Chapters 1 to 5.
2. Philip Parker, *Electronics*. London: Edward Arnold, 1950, Chapters 4, 5, and 8.
3. *RCA receiving tube manual.* Harrison, N.J.: Radio Corporation of America, 1964.
4. *Mullard technical handbook*, Volumes 1 and 3. London: Mullard, Ltd., 1964.
5. *Radio valve data.* Compiled by the staff of "Wireless World." London: Iliffe Books, Ltd., latest edition. (For tables of tube and semiconductor characteristics and lists of equivalent types.)

Transistors and Other Semiconductor Devices

....

3a   INTRODUCTION

Semiconductors are crystalline materials whose ability to conduct electricity depends on the excitation of electrons from one energy band to another within the crystal.[1] If electrons are able to be excited from localized atomic orbitals into a vacant band which extends throughout the crystal, they can move from one end of the crystal to the other when an external field is applied, and the material is termed an *n-type* semiconductor (Fig. 3.1*a*). Alternatively, electrons may be excited from a filled band which extends throughout the crystal into other more or less localized orbitals.   The "positive holes" which are left behind in the filled band can then move from one end of the crystal to the other under the influence of an external field, and the material is termed a *p-type* semiconductor (Fig. 3.1*b*). In either case the conductivity of the material increases when it is heated because the number of electrons excited is proportional to the Boltzmann factor $e^{-\Delta E/kT}$.   This increase is in marked contrast to the behavior of metallic conductors, whose conductivity decreases with increasing temperature.   The excitation process can usually be brought about by absorption of light, as well as thermally, so that many semiconductors are also photoconductors.

[1] See, for example, D. A. Wright, *Semiconductors*, London: Methuen & Co., 1950, or R. A. Smith, *Semiconductors*, London: Cambridge University Press, 1959.

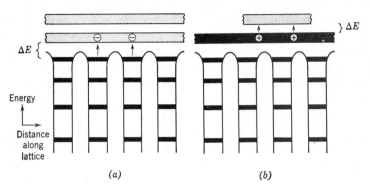

Fig. 3.1 Energy bands in semiconductors: (a) n-type and (b) p-type. Filled energy bands are shown in black, unfilled bands in gray. Potential wells correspond to positions of atoms on lattice sites. ↑ = electron excited, ⊖ = n-type carrier, ⊕ = p-type carrier.

Materials can be classified as either intrinsic or extrinsic semiconductors, depending on whether the observed conductivity is a property of the pure material or is due to the presence of donor or acceptor impurities in the crystal lattice. Such impurities can act either by donating electrons to vacant conduction bands or by accepting electrons from filled conduction bands. For example, an aluminum atom in a silicon crystal lattice has one less valence electron than is required for bonding to each of its four nearest neighbors. This atom readily accepts an electron from the lattice, leaving behind a positive hole which can migrate from one atom to another throughout the crystal. Similarly, an arsenic impurity atom in a silicon lattice has one valence electron too many, and it readily transfers this to the lattice, so turning the material into an n-type semiconductor.

The solid-state electronic devices which are based on semiconductors are essentially single crystals in which certain regions are of n-type character and others are of p-type character. Extrinsic semiconductors are used for making these devices, since their p or n character can be controlled by fixing the nature of the impurities in the host lattice. The host material is normally either germanium or silicon, germanium being the more widely used for making transistors, as it presents fewer technological problems and the final product is therefore considerably cheaper. The host material is first purified, e.g., by zone melting (the concentration of unwanted impurities must be below 1 part in 10^{10}), and then the required amount of donor or acceptor impurity is added. Phosphorus, arsenic, and antimony are commonly used as donors, and boron, aluminum, gallium, and indium as acceptors. Details of the various processes which are used to produce crystals with controlled n- and p-type regions may be found in several of the references given at the end of this chapter.

Even in the absence of impurities germanium and silicon conduct electricity to a small extent, because electrons can be excited thermally from one band to another with the creation of an electron-hole pair. This leads to the presence of a small number of *minority carriers*, for example, positive holes in n-type material. The number of minority carriers depends on the size of the energy gap ΔE in the pure crystal. In germanium the energy gap is 0.72 eV, while in silicon it is 1.03 eV, so that at room temperature there are far fewer (10^{-5} times) minority carriers in silicon than in germanium.

In the next section we describe the semiconductor diode, which is the simplest electronic device to make use of the properties we have been discussing. After the diode we shall consider the transistor, which can be regarded as the semiconductor counterpart of the pentode tube. Then we shall briefly describe the silicon-controlled rectifier and the Zener diode—analogous to the thyratron and the voltage reference tube respectively—together with some other solid-state, semiconductor devices which have no exact counterparts among vacuum tubes. In the last section of this chapter the relative advantages and disadvantages of corresponding types of vacuum tubes and solid-state devices will be summarized.

3b   THE SEMICONDUCTOR DIODE

Suppose that an n-type and a p-type region are in contact, as in Fig. 3.2. If a potential difference is applied to the crystal in the direction which is indicated in the figure, the free electrons and positive holes will both migrate towards the junction, where recombination will occur. Electrons will be removed at the positive terminal, with the creation of new positive holes, and electrons will be injected into the lattice at the negative terminal. A current will

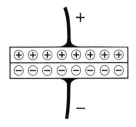

Fig. 3.2   Semiconductor diode.

therefore flow through the crystal, the resistance to a voltage applied in this direction being only of the order of a hundred ohms or less. If the electrical connections are now reversed, the positive and negative majority carriers migrate away from the junction, leaving a *depletion layer.* The resistance of the depletion layer is very high (in excess of a megohm) because conduction in this layer is dependent on the presence of the relatively few minority carriers. Therefore the device behaves as a diode, effectively conducting electricity in one direction only, and can be used for the same purposes as the vacuum diodes which were discussed in Chapter 2.

It is important that the electrical connections to the crystal at the positive and negative terminals should be purely ohmic contacts, i.e., that they should not possess any *n/p* character. This can be achieved, for example, by using an acceptor material for making contact to the *p*-type region and a donor material for making contact to the *n*-type region.

The circuit symbol and a typical current-voltage characteristic for a semiconductor diode are shown in Fig. 3.3.   The symbol is written with the solid arrow pointing in the direction in which the conventional positive current would prefer to flow, i.e., the arrowhead corresponds to the anode of a vacuum diode.   When the diode is connected in the direction of easy current flow, it is said to be *forward-biased.* If it is connected in the opposite direction, it is said to be *reverse-biased.*   Both forward and reverse characteristics are given in the data provided by the makers, as in Fig. 3.3.   In the forward direction the current increases roughly exponentially with voltage, but in the reverse direction a small saturation current is reached when the applied voltage is very small, and this current remains practically

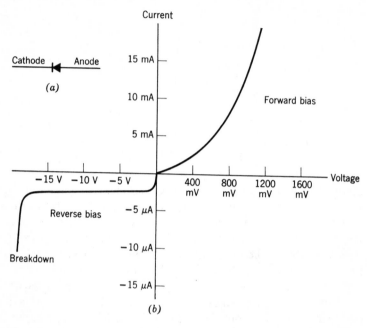

Fig. 3.3   (a) Circuit symbol for a semiconductor diode.   (b) Representative characteristics of a semiconductor diode.   The breakdown voltage (and corresponding peak inverse voltage rating) can be much higher than is indicated here.

constant as the voltage is increased.   If the inverse voltage becomes too great, the device first breaks down and becomes a short circuit, after which it may burn out and become an open circuit.

3c   THE TRANSISTOR

A transistor is a three-layer device, with ohmic connections provided to each of the three layers.   The layers may be in the order *pnp*, as in Fig. 3.4a, or *npn* as in Fig. 3.4b.   Most of the transistors that are encountered in practice are of the *pnp* type.   In both types the relatively thin middle layer is known as the *base*, while one of the outer layers forms the *emitter* and the other the *collector*.

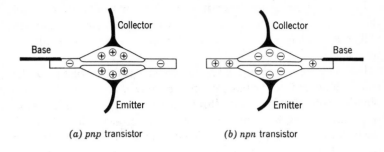

(a) *pnp* transistor   (b) *npn* transistor

Fig. 3.4   Cross sections of alloy-junction transistors.

The circuit symbols for *pnp* and *npn* transistors are given in Figs. 3.5*a* and 3.5*b*, respectively.   When transistors are in operation the polarities of the applied voltages are as shown here.   It should be noted that when the transistor is in operation the emitter-base section constitutes a forward-biased diode, and the direction of the arrow in the circuit symbol corresponds to the preferred direction of flow of positive current through this diode.   The collector-base section, on the other hand, constitutes a reverse-biased diode, so that most of the voltage between collector and emitter actually appears across the collector-base junction.   If we wish to compare the transistor with a vacuum tube, the base is the control element analogous to a grid, the emitter is roughly analogous to the cathode, and the collector corresponds to the anode.

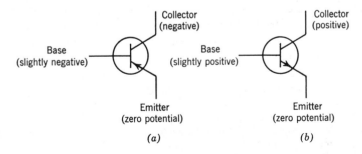

(a)   (b)

Fig. 3.5   Circuit symbols for transistors: (a) *pnp*, (b) *npn*.

In order to see qualitatively how a transistor works, we consider the example of a *pnp* transistor (Fig. 3.4*a*). The same explanation will apply to an *npn* transistor but with positive and negative voltages reversed.

Under the influence of the applied voltage positive holes from the emitter migrate into the base, where they may either undergo recombination with electrons, since this is an *n*-type region, or else diffuse right through the base into the depletion layer at the junction with the collector.[2] The base is intentionally made very thin so that there is a good chance the positive holes will get through without recombination taking place. Once they have reached the collector depletion layer, the electric field takes over and sweeps them into the collector. With no positive holes coming from the emitter, the only current in the reverse-biased base-collector diode is due to the minority carriers in these two regions and is necessarily very small. It follows that the size of the collector current is largely governed by the rate at which positive holes from the emitter can traverse the base.

Within the base region the crystal lattice as a whole must remain electrically neutral; therefore the number of positive holes in the base must equal the number of free electrons, which in turn is governed by the size of the external negative potential that has been applied to the base. Making the base more negative has the effect of injecting more electrons into the lattice, thus permitting the concentration of positive holes in the base region to increase. To use a very simple picture, the rate at which positive holes traverse the base region is given by

$$i_+ = C \cdot v/t \qquad (3.1)$$

where C is the concentration of positive holes in the base, v their mean velocity due to the diffusion gradient, and t the effective thickness of the base. Hence the increase in C that results from making the base more negative leads to a corresponding increase in the collector current.

If the collector-base voltage is increased, the velocity v does not

---

[2] There is another less important depletion layer at the emitter junction because of electrons diffusing from the base into the emitter and holes diffusing from the emitter into the base. This diffusion continues in the absence of any external voltage until the resulting potential gradient (produced by the separation of charges) is sufficient to counteract the concentration gradients.

increase appreciably since practically all the voltage appears across the depletion layer at the collector junction, but the thickness of the depletion layer increases. This increase in the thickness of the depletion layer subtracts from the base thickness t that has to be traversed, and the net result is a small increase in the collector current.

To maintain a steady concentration of free electrons in the base region, it is necessary to provide a current of electrons into the base to make up for those that are lost by recombination with positive holes. Thus the transistor behaves essentially as a current amplifier, the size of the collector current being determined by the size of the base current. The ratio of collector current to base current is termed the *current gain* of the transistor. To take some typical figures, suppose that 2% of the positive holes undergo recombination in the base region. Then if the emitter current is 1.00 mA, the collector current is 0.98 mA, the base current is 0.02 mA, and the current gain is 49.

The collector characteristics of a typical low-power transistor (Mullard OC75) are shown in Fig. 3.6. They are seen to be very similar to the anode characteristics of a pentode (Fig. 2.12) except that the curves are labeled with the value of the base current instead of with the grid voltage. A second important difference is that the voltages involved are very much lower than in the pentode case. Thus the knee of a pentode characteristic comes at about $+20$ V, whereas here it comes at about -200 mV. (The difference in sign arises because we are dealing with a *pnp* transistor.)

The *transfer* and *input* characteristics of this transistor are shown in Figs. 3.7 and 3.8, respectively. The form of the transfer characteristic shows that the collector current varies linearly with the base current. The form of the input characteristic, on the other hand, reveals that the dependence of the base current on the emitter-base voltage is nonlinear over much of the useful current range, although for a small voltage range a linear approximation would probably be satisfactory.

Transistor specifications are usually provided by the manufacturers in greater detail than are tube specifications. One reason for giving more detailed specifications is that there is an extra variable, namely the base current, to control the behavior of the device. A second reason is that transistors of any particular type show a much greater spread of characteristics than do tubes of one type, and it is

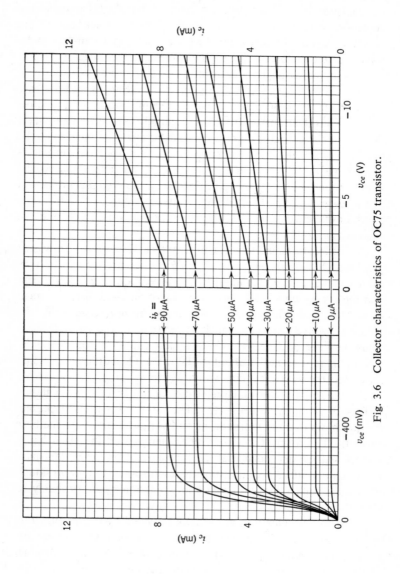

Fig. 3.6   Collector characteristics of OC75 transistor.

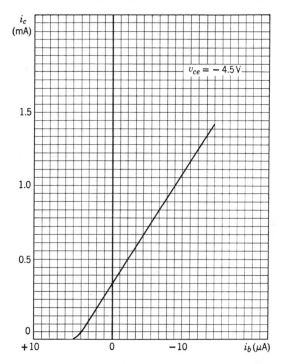

Fig. 3.7 Transfer characteristic of OC75 transistor.

necessary for the circuit designer to be aware of the variations that are likely to be encountered. A third factor is that the properties of semiconductors are very dependent on temperature, so that it is necessary to know, for example, the maximum permissible power dissipation in the transistor as a function of the ambient temperature. The last two factors are particularly important in the commercial production of transistorized equipment. In commercial production it is necessary to obtain the maximum performance from every circuit component in order to achieve low cost, but is also necessary to allow for the worst possible combination of circuit parameters, because of the spread in the characteristics of components, in order to achieve high reliability. These factors will carry less weight in the construction of "homemade" laboratory equipment, for individual attention can then be given to each component, and long-term reliability can

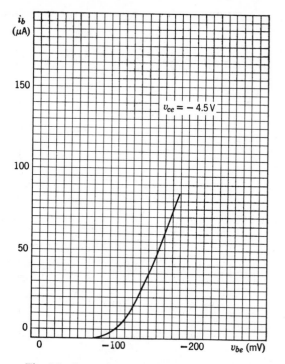

Fig. 3.8   Input characteristic of OC75 transistor.

be obtained (at slightly increased cost) by choosing components that have somewhat higher ratings than necessary.

A very large number of parameters have been defined for describing the response of transistors to small input signals.[3]   We shall endeavor to get by with a minimum number of these.   The most important is the *small-signal current gain* β, which is given by

$$\beta = \left(\frac{\partial i_c}{\partial i_b}\right)_{v_{ce}} \tag{3.2}$$

Here i_c is the collector current, i_b the base current, and v_{ce} the collector to emitter voltage.   This parameter may also be designated by the symbols α' and h_{fe} (in the "hybrid" system — see Appendix 2).

<hr />

[3] See, for example, *GE transistor manual*.   Syracuse, N.Y.: General Electric Company, Sixth Edition, 1962, p. 55.   See also Appendices 2 and 3.

It is a pure number having a value which lies in the range from about 10 to 250, values near 50 being most common. A second important parameter is the *forward-current transfer ratio* α, which may also be designated by the symbol h_{fb}. It is defined by the equation

$$\alpha = \left(\frac{\partial i_c}{\partial i_e}\right)_{v_{cb}} \tag{3.3}$$

where i_e is the emitter current and the other symbols have the same meanings as before. This parameter is also a pure number, with a value between about 0.95 and 0.995. Since the emitter current is equal to the sum of the collector and base currents, it follows that

$$\beta = \frac{\alpha}{1 - \alpha} \tag{3.4}$$

These parameters can also be defined for large changes in collector current. The resulting *large-signal parameters* are distinguished by placing a bar over the greek letter, as $\bar{\alpha}$, or by writing h_{FE} and h_{FB} instead of h_{fe} and h_{fb}. The large-signal parameters, which essentially give the ratios of the various currents near the middle of the useful operating range, are often the only parameters specified for a switching transistor.

A third parameter, which commonly appears in formulas for the voltage gain of transistor amplifiers, is the *base input resistance* $r_{be} = (\partial v_{be}/\partial i_b)_{v_{ce}}$, where v_{be} is the base-emitter voltage. (In the hybrid system this parameter is h_{ie}.) The value of this parameter varies from less than 10 ohms, for power transistors having collector currents of several amperes, to as much as 2000 ohms for low-current, small-signal transistors having collector currents of a few milliamperes.

For many purposes the only parameter it is *essential* to keep in mind is the current gain β.

In terms of the large-signal parameters we can write

$$i_c = \bar{\alpha} i_e + i_{cbo} \tag{3.5}$$

or

$$i_c = \bar{\beta} i_b + i'_{cbo} \tag{3.6}$$

where i_{cbo} is the reverse-bias *leakage current* through the collector-base junction, and

$$i'_{cbo} = i_{cbo}(1 + \bar{\beta}) \tag{3.7}$$

This leakage current amounts to an internal base current which, because it increases with increasing temperature, has a marked effect on the thermal stability of transistor circuits (cf. the discussion of thermal runaway in section 4c).

At very high frequencies the response of a transistor is limited by the time taken for carriers to diffuse across the base region. To obtain the best high-frequency characteristics it is therefore necessary to have the thinnest possible base region. The high-frequency behavior of a transistor is commonly specified by stating the α-*cutoff frequency* f_α, which is the frequency at which α has fallen to 0.707 of its low-frequency value.

3d   OTHER SEMICONDUCTOR DEVICES

The Silicon-Controlled Rectifier. The silicon-controlled rectifier (SCR) is a four-layer *pnpn* device whose characteristics are very similar to those of a thyratron tube. A diagram of a cross section through a typical SCR and the corresponding circuit symbol are given in Fig. 3.9.

If a voltage is applied in the reverse direction, the SCR behaves in the same manner as an ordinary rectifier, since it consists of two reverse-biased diodes in series. If a voltage is applied in the forward direction, the SCR has only two stable states, OFF and ON. How

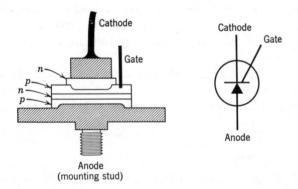

Fig. 3.9   Cross section and circuit symbol of a silicon-controlled rectifier.

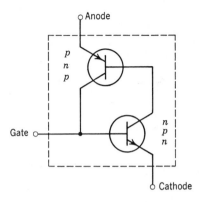

Fig. 3.10   Two-transistor equivalent of SCR.

this comes about can be appreciated by regarding the device as the equivalent of two silicon transistors, one *npn* and the other *pnp*, connected together as in Fig. 3.10.

If no current flows into the base of the *npn* transistor, then no current, apart from the very small leakage current due to minority carriers, flows in the collector circuit of this transistor. Therefore none flows in the base or collector circuits of the *pnp* transistor, and the device is in the OFF or "forward blocking state." If now a few positive holes are injected into the base of the *npn* transistor via the gate, the amplified base current flows in the collector circuit and so through the base of the *pnp* transistor. This current is further amplified and injected back into the base of the *npn* transistor, so that the current through the device continues to build up until it is limited by the resistance of the external circuit. This is the ON condition. The OFF state is a stable one because α for a silicon transistor falls off sharply at low values of the emitter current. Hence any small currents produced by statistical fluctuations in the concentrations of positive holes or free electrons are swallowed up by recombination, rather than being amplified, and the SCR remains in the OFF condition. In the ON condition a certain minimum current, the *holding current*, must flow through the device or it will turn itself off because of this effect.

If the forward voltage is made very high while the gate is closed, the minority carriers may gain sufficient energy to forcibly liberate

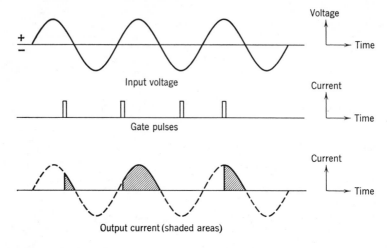

Input voltage

Gate pulses

Output current (shaded areas)

Fig. 3.11   Controlled rectification with an SCR.

majority carriers in the gate region, in which case the SCR will turn itself on.   The voltage which is required to do this is termed the "forward breakover voltage."

The most valuable characteristic of silicon-controlled rectifiers is their ability to initiate a very large current flow as a result of having received a relatively small amount of trigger current. (Typical figures are gate pulse 50 mA, total current up to 200 amperes.) They have found wide application as power controls, relays, and voltage regulators.   SCR's are particularly useful as controlled rectifiers of alternating current, since they can be turned on by means of the gate for any desired fraction of the positive half cycle and are turned off automatically during each negative half cycle.   The power delivered by the circuit is then governed by the length of time for which the gate is open.   This mode of operation is illustrated in Fig. 3.11.

The Silicon-Controlled Switch.   The silicon-controlled switch is similar to the silicon-controlled rectifier except that gate connections are provided to both base layers.   This is illustrated, with the corresponding circuit symbol, in Fig. 3.12.   The provision of the extra gate lead gives the device additional versatility.   It can be used in the same manner as the SCR to act as a very sensitive switch-

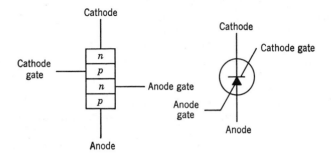

Fig. 3.12   Silicon-controlled switch.

ing element, but with the advantage that it can be switched off as well as on by means of signals applied to the gates.[4]

The Unijunction Transistor.   The circuit symbol and a diagram of the construction of the unijunction transistor are given in Fig. 3.13. The three terminals are called the emitter, base 1, and base 2.   In normal operation base 1 is grounded, and a positive voltage bias V_{BB} is applied to base 2 (Fig. 3.14).   The base acts as a simple voltage divider, the *interbase resistance* R_{BB} being of the order of 5000 ohms. The resulting potential at the emitter contact is equal to ηV_{BB}, where η is termed the *intrinsic standoff ratio* and is a constant, independent of V_{BB}.

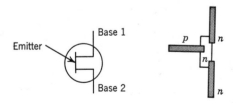

Fig. 3.13   Circuit symbol and construction of a unijunction transistor.

[4] Another variant of this type of device, the *thyristor*, has a single base connection and behaves as a conventional high-speed transistor at low collector currents.   At high collector currents (above the "breakover" point) it switches to a stable ON state.   It can be turned OFF by applying a reverse trigger to the base.   (*RCA transistor manual.*)

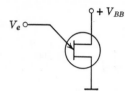

Fig. 3.14 Biasing of a unijunction transistor.

If the emitter diode is initially reverse-biased because V_e is less than ηV_{BB}, no current will flow in the emitter circuit. Once the

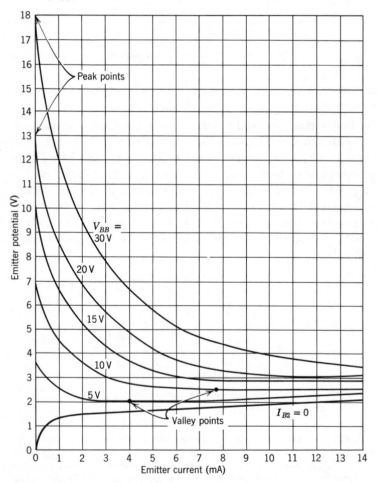

Fig. 3.15 Unijunction transistor; emitter input characteristics.

Anode

B

Cathode

Fig. 3.16 Circuit symbol for a Zener diode (B = breakdown).

"peak point" voltage ηV_{BB} is exceeded, however, current flows from e to b_1, and the voltage falls because the resistance offered to the current is only that of a forward-biased diode. This leads to the characteristics illustrated in Fig. 3.15. The unijunction transistor is therefore able to deliver a pulse of current when the emitter voltage exceeds some predetermined value, and one of its common uses is to provide a trigger pulse for a silicon-controlled rectifier.

The Zener Diode. The Zener, or breakdown, diode is the semiconductor counterpart of the voltage reference tube. The circuit symbol for this device is given in Fig. 3.16, and it should be noted that it is connected with the arrowhead pointing the opposite way around from a normal rectifying diode.

If the potential difference across a reverse-biased diode is increased beyond a certain point, breakdown occurs. This may be true Zener breakdown, caused by quantum-mechanical tunneling of electrons from one energy band to another, or avalanche breakdown caused by energy derived from minority carriers moving at high speed through the lattice. In either case the breakdown current increases very rapidly in proportion to the voltage increase beyond the breakdown point, and the resulting characteristic (Fig. 3.17) is very similar to that of a voltage reference tube.

Zener diodes are available to supply reference voltages at almost any value in the interval from about 1 to 200 V. In the upper part of this range voltage reference tubes can also be used and are often preferred. The simplest circuit for obtaining a steady reference voltage from a Zener diode is shown in Fig. 3.18. With this arrangement voltage fluctuations in the input largely appear across the resistance R, since the dynamic impedance ($\partial v/\partial i$) of the Zener diode is very low at the preferred operating current.

The Tunnel Diode. The tunnel diode is an extremely small *pn* device which is useful at ultrahigh frequencies, and even into the microwave

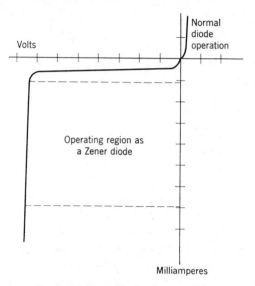

Fig. 3.17   Zener diode characteristic.

range (1000 Mc/sec, or more).   The p and n regions contain very high concentrations of impurities, so that when reverse bias is applied the depletion layer is so narrow that electrical charges can cross the junction by quantum-mechanical tunneling.   Hence the device conducts readily in the reverse direction.   This tunneling behavior is also important at small values of forward bias, and gives rise to a large initial peak in the current-voltage characteristic, superimposed on the normal exponential curve.   The circuit symbol and a typical characteristic for a tunnel diode are shown in Fig. 3.19.

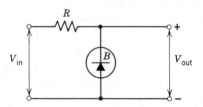

Fig. 3.18   Circuit for obtaining a steady voltage from a Zener diode.

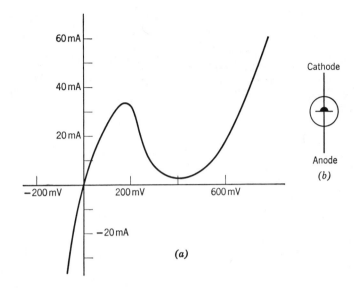

(a)

(b)

Cathode

Anode

Fig. 3.19   Tunnel diode: (*a*) typical characteristic, (*b*) circuit symbol.

The negative resistance region in the characteristic, coming just after the initial peak, gives the tunnel diode its ability to act as an amplifier, oscillator, or high-frequency switch.   In the latter role the tunnel diode is particularly suitable for computer applications because of its small size, high speed, and low power consumption.   For further details and typical circuits the reader should consult reference 6 in the list given at the end of this chapter.

The Field-Effect Transistor.   This device is similar to the unijunction transistor, in that it consists of a bar of *n*-type material, usually silicon, with ohmic contacts at either end and a *p*-type contact near the middle.   In this case, however, the *p*-type contact is made from both sides of the bar in such a way that there is only a narrow channel of *n*-type material at the center of the bar.   If the *pn* junction is reverse-biased, the resulting depletion layer will subtract from the channel thickness, and the number of electrons which can flow from one end of the bar (the *source*) to the other end (the *drain*) therefore can be controlled by the amount of negative potential which is applied to the *gate*.   Because the gate junction is reverse-biased, the input impedance is high (typically >5 M), and the characteristics of the device are more like those of a tube than those of a transistor (Fig. 3.20). The field-effect transistor obviously has many potential applications in situations where the low input impedance of ordinary transistors is a major disadvantage. In addition, the field-effect transistor (abbreviated FET) is markedly superior to the ordinary

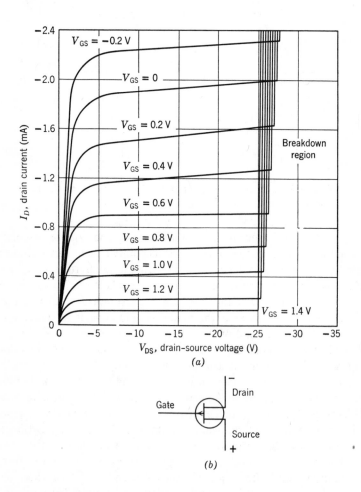

(a)

(b)

Fig. 3.20   Field-effect transistor: (a) typical characteristics, (b) circuit symbol for a p-channel FET (Texas Instruments type 2N2497).

junction transistor in its internal noise characteristics (see Chapter 8) and resistance to damage by high-energy radiation. The description just given of the operation of the device applies to an "*n*-channel" FET; for a *p*-channel FET the operation is the same except that voltage polarities are reversed. For further details see reference 8 at the end of this chapter.

3e RELATIVE MERITS OF TUBES AND SEMICONDUCTOR DEVICES

Semiconductor devices, and transistors in particular, have a number of advantages over vacuum tubes, the most obvious being their small size. This small size, combined with extreme reliability and low power dissipation, is responsible for the fact that vacuum tubes have been completely superseded by solid-state components in high-speed digital computers, and in other applications where very large numbers of circuit elements are required to work together, or where space is at a premium.[5]

Vacuum tubes, because of their glass envelopes, are very fragile in comparison with solid-state devices and are subject to *microphonics*, i.e., noise introduced into the output as a result of vibration of the electrodes relative to one another when the equipment is bumped or jarred. They can break down because the heater fails, because gas enters the envelope, or because the cathode emitting surface is poisoned, none of which can affect a transistor. An obvious consequence of the presence of a heated filament is the generation of heat, and the necessity of getting rid of this can be a considerable nuisance in large pieces of equipment—probably more so than with transistors, where the main problem is one of getting heat out of the device itself and away from the temperature-sensitive junctions. Because the heaters of vacuum tubes are usually operated from low-voltage ac supplies, there may be additional trouble from mains hum, i.e., the appearance in the output of a 50- or 60-cycle signal derived from the heaters as a result of unintentional inductive coupling ("pickup").

[5] The possibilities for miniaturization are exploited to the full in such devices as "grown solid-state circuits," in which a whole amplifier or switching circuit is contained in a tiny crystal wafer. See, for example, *Catalogue, semiconductor components*, Texas Instruments Incorporated, Dallas, 1965, and reference 7 (see list at the end of this chapter), Chapter 19.

Transistors in general are low-impedance devices, i.e., they operate with low voltages and high currents, whereas vacuum tubes are high-impedance devices, requiring high voltages for relatively low currents. Thus vacuum tubes have considerable advantages for dealing with high voltages or with very small currents in high-impedance circuits, but more careful insulation is necessary with the higher voltages and impedances that tubes require. Transistor circuits are probably safer in that they can usually be handled while the power is on without the handler suffering any ill effects. The lower voltage requirement also means that transistorized equipment can be economically run from batteries rather than from bulky (unless transistorized!) mains-operated power supplies. A further consequence of the lower impedance is that transistorized circuits are less subject to undesirable electromagnetic pickup from ac mains, other electrical equipment, or local radio stations. However, transistors tend to be noisier than tubes for other reasons (see Chapter 8).

Vacuum diodes have an obvious advantage over semiconductor diodes in that their reverse resistance is effectively infinite. Not only is the reverse resistance of a solid-state diode considerably less than infinite, but it decreases markedly with increasing temperature (but the forward resistance is also greater for a vacuum diode). This sensitivity to temperature is a fault that is common to all semiconductor devices. In transistors it leads to the possibility of *thermal runaway*, which can occur when a transistor is being used close to its limits of operation. The parameter β increases with rising temperatures, thus increasing the collector current which results from a given external base current. The increased collector current dissipates more power, which in turn increases the temperature of the transistor, thus causing a further rise in β, and so on. If nothing else, the need to avoid this sort of disaster makes extra work for the circuit designer. Furthermore, if appreciable power is to be dissipated, a transistor needs to be mounted on some form of heat sink, largely negating the advantage transistors have over tubes in not requiring special mounting sockets.

One situation in which solid-state devices appear to have serious inherent disadvantages is in the presence of high-energy radiation. Crystalline materials are liable to suffer from radiation-induced crystal defects—in severe cases a solid may be pushed right out of shape by stresses resulting from the presence of such defects. With transistors this internal degradation is produced most rapidly by irradiation with fast neutrons, and the effects of such irradiation are cumulative. Usually the first result is a decrease in the current gain β. Temporary malfunction can result from transient pulses of gamma radiation, which produce surface and internal ionization and hence increased leakage current. . This temporary trouble can sometimes induce thermal runaway and so cause permanent damage. At present there are insufficient data on the susceptibility of semiconductor devices to this type of failure, but they are much more susceptible than vacuum tubes.

The foregoing discussion illustrates the fact that the day of the final takeover of electronics by solid-state devices has not yet arrived. For a number of applications, especially those involving high voltages or very small currents, vacuum tubes are to be preferred, and in many other applications the competition is still so close that it may be better to capitalize on the forty years of experience that engineers have had with tubes rather than attempt to produce similar results with the less well-characterized transistors. For this reason we have described both kinds of device, and will continue to consider both transistor and vacuum tube circuits, side by side, throughout the remainder of the book.

EXERCISES

3.1 Look up the characteristics of different types of semiconductor devices, including both power and low-level transistors, in appropriate manuals. Interpret the data which are presented as well as you are able.

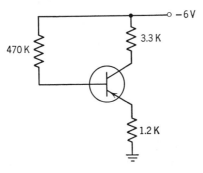

Ex. 3.2

3.2   The transistor in the circuit shown on p. 61 has $\alpha = 0.99$.   What is the value of β?   Neglecting the forward resistance of the emitter-base diode, calculate the currents and voltages at emitter, base, and collector.

3.3   In this circuit the input voltage varies between 8 and 12 V, the load R' is 1000 ohms, and the Zener diode gives a reference output of 6.0 V over the range 5 to 25 mA.   Calculate a suitable value for R.

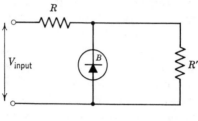

Ex. 3.3

3.4   Verify that in this circuit if R_{in} is much greater than the base input resistance $(\partial v_{be}/\partial i_b)_{vce}$, then $dV_{\text{out}}/dV_{\text{in}} = -\beta R_L/R_{\text{in}}$.

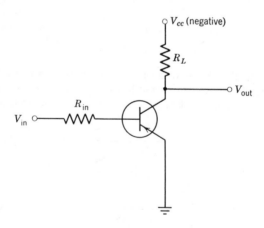

Ex. 3.4

3.5   Look up the characteristics of suitable Zener diodes and assess the worth of the following circuit for obtaining a reference voltage which is almost independent of temperature changes.

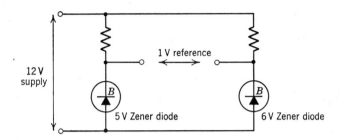

Ex. 3.5

REFERENCES

1. E. Wolfendale, *The transistor*. London: Heywood and Company, 1963, Chapters 1 and 4.
2. *Mullard reference manual of transistor circuits*. London: Mullard, Ltd., 1960, Chapters 1 and 4.
3. *GE transistor manual*. Syracuse N.Y.: General Electric Company, Sixth Edition, 1962, especially Chapters 1 to 4.
4. *RCA transistor manual*. Somerville, N.J.: Radio Corporation of America, 1964.
5. *GE controlled rectifier manual*. Auburn, N.Y.: General Electric Company, Second Edition, 1961.
6. *GE tunnel diode manual*. Liverpool, N.Y.: General Electric Company, 1961.
7. H. A. Romanowitz, *Fundamentals of semiconductor and tube electronics*. New York: John Wiley & Sons, Inc., 1962, Chapters 3 and 8.
8. W. Gosling, *Field-effect transistor applications*. London: Heywood and Company, 1964.

4

Tubes and Transistors as Amplifiers

4a INTRODUCTION

The most widely exploited property of vacuum tubes and transistors is their ability to be used as amplifiers. The function of an amplifier is to take a small signal and convert it into one that is large enough to do something useful, for example, to operate a meter, oscilloscope, pen recorder, or other output device, depending on the nature of the instrument in which the amplifier is incorporated. The type of amplifier which is preferred in a given situation depends on both the characteristics of the signal source and the type of output which is required, the nature of the signal source being the most important determining factor. It is often convenient in practice to use a separate *preamplifier* to match the characteristics of a specialized signal source, and to follow this with a more or less standard amplifier in order to bring the signal up to the desired final output level.

A general electronic instrument, such as is commonly encountered in research, would probably be organized according to the plan given in Fig. 4.1. In this *block diagram* the transducer is any device whose electrical properties are affected by the property of the system which is to be measured, for example, temperature, pressure, ion current, or optical density. In the simplest case the output device is just a meter. More elaborate instruments may have other transducers and amplifiers, may involve different types of input to the system, or may even use the output from an amplifier to control an input to the system.

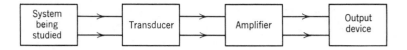

Fig. 4.1   Block diagram of a general electronic instrument.

An important feature of Fig. 4.1 is that each connection between one box and the next is drawn as a double line. This corresponds to the fact that when a change in some property is being measured there must be a reference point against which to compare it. (In electrical instruments this reference point is usually, though not invariably, earth potential.) An amplifier can therefore be regarded externally as a four-terminal "black box," while from the electrical point of view the transducer and output device are two-terminal black boxes. The input terminals of the amplifier and output-device boxes may be characterized by the *input impedance* Z_i which they present to an incoming signal. The output terminals of the transducer and amplifier are similarly characterized by an *output impedance* Z_o, which is regarded as being in series with a voltage generator V_o which is responsible for the output signal. The output impedance governs the amount of power which this signal generator can deliver to the next circuit stage.[1] The output V_o is normally proportional to the chemical or physical input signal in a transducer and to the electrical input signal in an amplifier. In the latter the proportionality factor is termed the "amplifier gain." These statements are summarized in Fig. 4.2.

We observe that the input signal to any stage is given by $V_o Z_i' / (Z_i' + Z_o)$, where Z_i' is the input impedance and V_o and Z_o refer to the output of the preceding stage. Hence to obtain a maximum input voltage signal the input impedance should be large and the output impedance small. If, on the other hand, we wish to transfer as much power as possible from one stage to the next, the output impedance of one stage should be equal to the input impedance of the next in accordance with the maximum power theorem (Exercise

---

[1] This is the viewpoint which results from the application of Thevenin's theorem. An alternative point of view, which is often useful, is to regard the output signal as being due to a current generator, of infinite internal impedance, shunted by an *admittance* $Y_o = 1/Z_o$ (Norton's theorem).

4.1). This is often expressed by saying that for maximum signal power the input and output impedances should be *matched*.

In this chapter we shall consider a number of different types of amplifiers, using both tubes and transistors. The most important characteristics of each amplifier will be its gain, which may be expressed as voltage, current, or power gain, and its input and output impedances. A further important characteristic, which will be discussed in Chapter 8, is the bandwidth, i.e., the range of signal frequencies for which the amplifier gain is maintained.

The input and output impedances of single-stage amplifiers vary considerably according to the manner in which the tube or transistor is incorporated into the circuit. There are three basic ways of orienting a tube or transistor in relation to the input and output

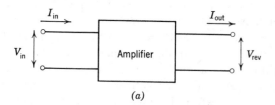

(a)

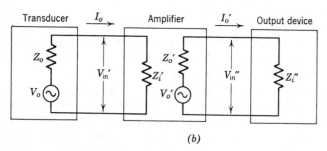

(b)

Fig. 4.2(a)   Input and output impedances:

$$Z_{in} = \left(\frac{\partial V_{in}}{\partial I_{in}}\right)_{V_{rev}}, \qquad Z_{out} = \left(\frac{\partial V_{rev}}{\partial I_{out}}\right)_{V_{in}}$$

where V_{in} is an external voltage applied to the input terminals and V_{rev} is an external voltage applied to the output terminals.

(b)   Input and output impedances:

$$V_0' = \text{Gain} \times \frac{V_0 Z_i'}{Z_i' + Z_0}, \qquad I_0 = \frac{V_0}{Z_0 + Z_i}$$

circuits, giving rise to what are known as the grounded-cathode, grounded-grid, and cathode-follower configurations for a tube, and the common (or "grounded") emitter, common-base, and emitter-follower (or "common-collector") configurations for a transistor. The different configurations are illustrated in Fig. 4.3.

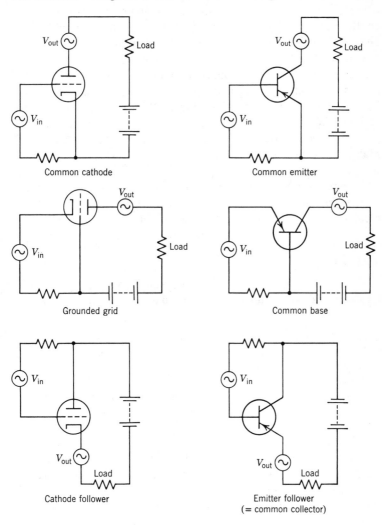

Fig. 4.3 Amplifier configurations.

In each configuration the output voltage is developed across a load resistor which is the main contributor to the output impedance of the amplifier (in the cathode-follower and emitter-follower configurations this resistor is shunted by the low forward impedance of the tube or transistor). The most widely used configuration is that with common cathode or emitter. In the common-cathode or common-emitter configuration the output impedance is high, the input impedance is high for a tube and moderately high for a transistor, and both current and voltage amplification are obtained. With common grid or common base the input impedance is low, the output impedance is very high for a tube and high for a transistor, the current gain is unity, and the voltage gain is high. With emitter follower and cathode follower the input impedance is very high, the output impedance is low, the voltage gain is unity, and the current gain is high. Thus, by suitable choice of tube or transistor configurations in one or more stages, it is possible to design an amplifier to have any desired combination of high or low input and output impedances and current or voltage gain. The essential features of the different configurations are summarized for convenience in Table 4.1.

Table 4.1

Configuration	Input Impedance	Output Impedance	Voltage Gain	Current Gain
Grounded cathode	high	high	high	high
Grounded grid	low	very high	high	1.0
Cathode follower	very high	low	1.0	high
Grounded emitter	fairly high	fairly high	high	high
Grounded base	low	high	high	1.0
Emitter follower	high	very low	1.0	high

In this chapter we shall go through the steps which are involved in designing an amplifier stage for each of the configurations listed in Table 4.1. We shall do this for actual tubes and transistors, using the data published by the manufacturers, so that after completing this chapter the reader should, at the very least, be able to select values for circuit components in order to suit the characteristics of other tubes or transistors in these configurations. In Chapter 5 we shall consider how to combine the individual amplifier stages into multistage amplifiers.

4b A PENTODE VOLTAGE AMPLIFIER

A typical circuit for a common-cathode amplifier, using a pentode, is shown in Fig. 4.4. For a triode the circuit would be the same except for the absence of screen and suppressor grid connections. The tube we shall use to illustrate the design procedure is an RCA type 6AU6. This is a sharp cutoff pentode, having a 6.3 V heater, and it is described in the tube manual as being suitable for use as a radio-frequency amplifier in compact radio equipment, especially in high-frequency, wide-band applications. Its choice presupposes that we are intending to build an amplifier for small signals, of amplitude perhaps a few millivolts peak to peak, and that we intend to work at high frequencies, or alternatively to obtain very faithful reproduction of nonsinusoidal signals at frequencies in the audio range (roughly 20 cycles to 20 kc/sec). The plate characteristics of this tube are shown in Fig. 4.5.

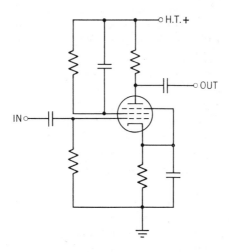

Fig. 4.4 Pentode common-cathode amplifier stage.

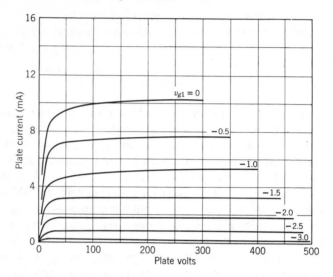

Fig. 4.5 Plate characteristics of type 6AU6 pentode. (Screen grid potential = 100 V.)

Since the input signal is to be of moderately high frequency, we can use small capacitors for coupling to the preceding and following stages, and we can leave the input and output dc voltage levels of this stage to adjust themselves independently. The coupling capacitors are chosen to be 0.1 μF, since this corresponds to a fairly low impedance in the audio-frequency range, and capacitors of a suitable voltage rating (say 450 V working) and conveniently small dimensions are readily available. The suppressor grid will be connected to the cathode, as is usual practice, and the output signal will be taken from the anode load. The supply voltage is assumed to be +300 V. We are now at the stage which is shown in Fig. 4.6.

The first major requirement is to decide on a suitable operating point for the tube. With pentodes the mutual conductance g_m falls off with decreasing anode current, so the latter should not be too low. According to the tube manual the maximum allowable plate dissipation (product of anode voltage and current) is 3.5 W. If the whole supply voltage were connected across the tube, this dissipation would correspond to a maximum allowable anode current of 11.5 mA,

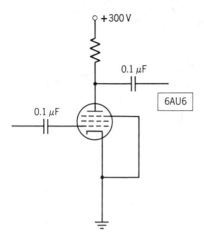

Fig. 4.6 Beginning of pentode amplifier
design.

and we shall find that this leaves us plenty of leeway.   Suppose that
the biggest input signal that is likely to be encountered is 0.5 V peak
to peak; then the largest positive excursion of the control grid is
expected to be 0.25 V.   Therefore, if we set the *grid bias* voltage
initially at −0.5 V, the input signal can be twice as large as is
anticipated before the output is distorted as a result of the grid
becoming positive with respect to the cathode.   At this value of grid
potential the plate current is 7.5 mA, which is considerably less than
the allowed maximum. According to the manual the current flowing
to the screen grid is now 3.0 mA, and the total cathode current is
therefore 10.5 mA.   In the plate characteristics of Fig. 4.5 some
curvature begins to become apparent at anode voltages below about
100 V, so the anode potential should be set at some value greater
than this in order to avoid distortion of the output.   The actual
value will be governed by the size of the anode load, and we shall
postpone a decision about this until a method of fixing the grid bias
has been chosen.

Three possible ways of fixing the grid bias at a suitable value are
illustrated in Fig. 4.7.   The first method, termed "self-bias" or
"cathode bias," involves connecting the grid to earth through a high
resistance and inserting a cathode resistor of such a size that the

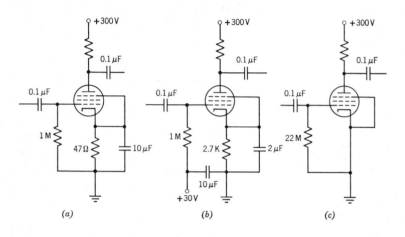

Fig. 4.7 Methods of obtaining grid bias: (*a*) cathode bias, grid at earth potential, (*b*) cathode bias, grid at +30 V, (*c*) grid resistor bias.

cathode current (sum of anode and screen grid currents) produces a potential difference across the cathode resistor which is equal to the desired bias voltage.   In the example shown in Fig. 4.7, the grid is at earth potential and the cathode is at +0.5 V.   The cathode resistor is bypassed with a 10 μF capacitor so that its potential will remain constant despite the variations in the anode current that are caused by an incoming signal.   The bypass capacitor is usually chosen so that its impedance is less than one-tenth that of the cathode resistor at the lowest frequency which is to be amplified.

The second method of Fig. 4.7 also uses self-bias, but in this case the grid resistor is connected to a source of a positive potential, +30 V in the present example.   This method makes the cathode current almost independent of the properties of the tube, since it is an important general rule that *the cathode potential always adjusts itself to be near that of the control grid while a tube is conducting.*   It is a good approximation here to say that the cathode potential is +30 V, so the cathode current is fixed at 30/2.7 = 11 mA.   If we refer to the characteristics we can now verify that, with allowance for the current to grid 2, the grid potential is −0.5 V with respect to the cathode.   Hence a better approximation to the cathode current is 30.5/2.7 = 11.3 mA.   This is the nearest we can get to the desired 10.5 mA, since the next larger preferred value[2] for the cathode resistor is 3.3 K.   As before, the cathode resistor is bypassed with a capacitor.

The third method is termed "grid resistor biasing." In this method, which is not recommended for amplifiers for scientific use (as opposed to light entertainment), a negative-bias voltage is provided by the flow of grid current through the high-valued grid resistor.

We choose the first method of fixing the grid bias. The dissipation in the 47 ohm resistor is only 5 milliwatts, so a $\frac{1}{4}$ or $\frac{1}{2}$ W resistor will be more than adequate. If the second method were used the dissipation in the cathode resistor would be 300 mW, which is really too much for a $\frac{1}{2}$ W resistor, especially if prolonged drifts in the amplifier during warming up are to be avoided. Therefore a 1 W, or better a 2 W, rating would need to be specified.

A suitable screen grid potential is found from the manual to be +125 V. The screen grid current has been stated to be 3.0 mA, so the power dissipation at this grid is 475 mW, which is less than the maximum permitted dissipation of 0.75 W. The easiest way to fix the potential of this grid is to connect it through a resistor to the 300 V supply. The value of the resistor works out to be $175/3 \times 10^3$, or 58 K, to which the nearest preferred value is 56 K. The power dissipation in the resistor is 0.525 W, so a 1 W (or a 2 W) rating is indicated. This resistor is also bypassed, with a 2 μF capacitor which may be taken either to ground or to the 300 V supply. If the 300 V supply were to come on before the cathode of the 6AU6 had had time to warm up, the potential of grid 2 would rise to +300 V, so best use is made of the voltage rating of the capacitor if it is connected to the 300 V line.

We have now reached the stage which is shown in Fig. 4.8. It only remains to specify the value of the anode load. This should be as large as possible, in order to obtain maximum gain, but not so large that the anode voltage is liable to fall below 100 V in the presence of an incoming signal. As a reasonable compromise we choose a value of 22 K, which gives an anode voltage of 125 V. The power dissipation in the load resistor is 1.24 W, so it would be best to specify a 5 W rating.

[2] Resistors, other than precision resistors, and capacitors smaller than 1 μF, are available at values which are multiples of numbers in the series 1.0, 1.2, 1.5, 1.8, 2.2, 2.7, 3.3, 3.9, 4.7, 5.6, 6.8, 8.2, 10. These are termed the *preferred values* of resistance and capacitance.

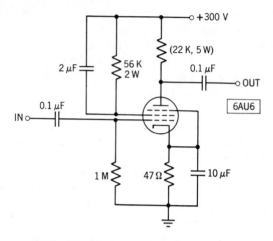

Fig. 4.8   Final pentode amplifier stage.

To calculate the amplifier gain we use the general equation (cf., section 2c)

$$di_a = \frac{dv_a}{\rho} + g_m \, dv_g \tag{4.1}$$

where

$$dv_a = -R_L \, di_a \tag{4.2}$$

Here i_a is the anode current, v_a the anode voltage, ρ the plate resistance ($= \partial v_a / \partial i_a$), v_g the grid voltage, g_m the mutual conductance, and R_L the anode load.   Hence the expression for the gain is found, by rearranging (4.1) and (4.2), to be

$$\frac{dv_a}{dv_g} = -g_m R_L \frac{\rho}{R_L + \rho} \tag{4.3}$$

where the minus sign indicates that the input and output signals are out of phase, i.e., when the grid voltage swings positive the anode voltage swings negative.   For the 6AU6 the plate resistance ρ is about 1.5 M, whereas R_L is only 22 K, so equation (4.3) reduces to the usual pentode expression

$$\frac{dv_a}{dv_g} = -g_m R_L \tag{4.4}$$

From the manual we find $g_m = 4.5 \times 10^{-3}$ ohm^{-1}, or 4.5 mA/V (this is actually stated in the manual in the barbarous form 4500 μmhos), so the voltage gain of the amplifier is -100, and a signal of 0.5 V peak to peak will therefore cause the anode potential to swing between 100 and 150 V. This result could also be estimated graphically by drawing the *load line*, whose equation is

$$v_a = v_{\text{supply}} - i_a R_L \qquad (4.5)$$

on top of the characteristic curves of Fig. 4.5, and noting the relative amounts of anode voltage and grid voltage which are swept out by a point as it moves along the load line. The graphical method, which is also applicable to transistor stages and is often highly convenient in practice, is described more fully in section 5c and will not be considered further in this chapter.

The input impedance of this amplifier at audio frequencies is effectively 1 M, since the grid-to-cathode impedance is very high so long as the grid-cathode diode has a reverse bias. (At high frequencies the interelectrode capacitances will contribute appreciably to the input and output impedances. See Chapter 8.) The output impedance is effectively equal to the load resistance of 22 K, since the plate resistance of the tube is very large. Note that from the point of view of the output the plate resistance is in parallel with the load resistance. Higher gain could be obtained from this tube, at the expense of increased output impedance (and decreased bandwidth), by scaling up the cathode resistor and the anode load. The black-box equivalent of this amplifier is shown in Fig. 4.9. If signals at very low frequencies are to be amplified, it is necessary to take the impedances of the coupling capacitors into account. The frequency limitations of amplifiers are discussed in some detail in Chapter 8.

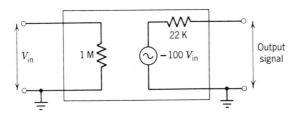

Fig. 4.9   Black-box equivalent of pentode amplifier stage.

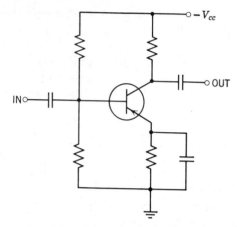

Fig. 4.10   Common-emitter amplifier.

4c   TRANSISTOR COMMON-EMITTER AMPLIFIER

This circuit (Fig. 4.10) is the transistor counterpart of the pentode amplifier we have just considered.   The transistor we shall use to illustrate the design procedure is an RCA type 2N175, which is specifically intended for use as an amplifier of small signals in the audio-frequency range.   Its collector characteristics are given in Fig. 4.11.

As with a tube amplifier, the first important thing to do is to select a suitable operating point.   The absolute maximum collector current is stated to be 2.0 mA, so it is safe to set the operating point at a collector current of 0.5 mA.   The supply voltage is -6 V, and the knee of the collector characteristic occurs at about -0.5 V, so -2.5 V is a reasonable choice for the collector-emitter voltage v_{ce}.   (The maximum rated value of v_{ce} is -10 V.)   This is normally chosen to be less than half the supply voltage, for reasons that will be explained shortly.   It helps to stabilize the operating point if there is a resistor between emitter and ground, but this resistor should not be too large because it reduces the possible size of the collector load resistor, upon which the voltage gain depends.   As a fair compromise we allow 2.5 V for the potential drop across the collector load and 1.0 V for the emitter load.   As with the pentode amplifier, the emitter resistor is bypassed with a capacitor.   Miniature high-value capacitors are

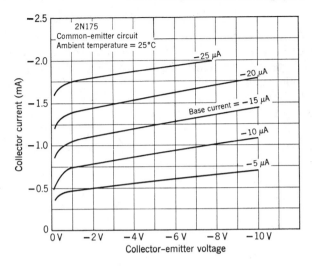

Fig. 4.11 Collector characteristics, 2N175 transistor.

available for the low working voltages commonly used in transistor circuits, and a value of 100 μF is selected. The impedance of this capacitor is only 75 ohms at a frequency of 20 cycles/sec. This is in line with the lower impedances which are characteristic of transistor

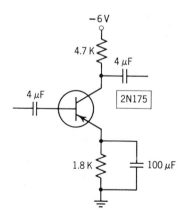

Fig. 4.12 Beginning of common-emitter amplifier circuit.

circuits, and for the same reason the coupling capacitors are chosen to be 4 μF. (These will be electrolytic capacitors, so it will be necessary to ensure that they are connected with correct polarity when this stage is being joined to the preceding and succeeding ones.) The circuit is now as shown in Fig. 4.12.

Further reference to the collector characteristics reveals that the base current at the operating point is -5 μA. This current has to flow from the base, which will be within a few millivolts of the emitter potential, i.e., at -1 V, to the -6 V supply. Hence we can use either a simple resistor to fix the base potential, as in Fig. 4.13a, or a potential divider, as in Fig. 4.13b.

Both of the arrangements in Fig. 4.13 will serve to fix the operating

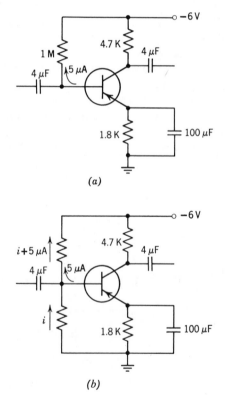

Fig. 4.13   Alternative biasing arrangements for a transistor.

point of the transistor, but the second, in which the resistance values in the potential divider still have to be specified, is the better one because it makes the operating point relatively independent of variations in β. Such variations can occur as a result of changes in the ambient temperature or the substitution of one transistor for another. The degree of improvement from adding the base-to-ground resistor increases as the resistance of the potential divider is decreased, but if the resistance is made too small, not only will battery drain become excessive but much of the input signal will be shunted away from the base. In the present instance we shall use the second method and allow for a current of 0.1 mA through the potential divider. This is twenty times greater than the anticipated base current, so if the base current changes by 10% as the result of a variation in the value of β, the base potential will change by only 0.5%. Since the emitter potential is practically the same as that of the base, and the emitter current is fixed by the values of the emitter resistor and the emitter potential, the current at the operating point will also change by only 0.5% as a result of a 10% change in β. A simple calculation now yields the resistance values which are given in Fig. 4.14. The power dissipation in the resistors is only a few milliwatts, so that $\frac{1}{4}$ W or even smaller resistors can be used in order to save space.

Before proceeding further it will be as well to examine the possibility that this amplifier might undergo "thermal runaway" and incinerate the transistor. We shall carry out the analysis in

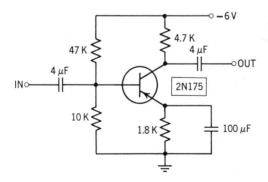

Fig. 4.14 Final common-emitter amplifier stage.

general terms so our conclusions will not be restricted to the present circuit.

Let T_{amb} and T_j be the ambient temperature and collector junction temperature, respectively, let θ be the rise in the junction temperature above ambient per watt of collector dissipation (usually quoted as the thermal resistance in °C/W), and let P_c be the collector dissipation in watts. Then at thermal equilibrium

$$T_j = T_{amb} + \theta P_c \tag{4.6}$$

Now if a small fluctuation $+\delta T_j$ produces an increase δP_c in the collector dissipation (because of an increase in the leakage current i_{cbo}), this will produce a further increase $\theta \, \delta P_c$ in the junction temperature. This new temperature rise will then lead to a further increase $\delta' P_c$ in the power dissipation, and so on. Hence, since we can write

$$\delta P_c = \frac{\partial P_c}{\partial T_j} \, \delta T_j$$

the junction temperature will finally tend to a value

$$T_j' = T_j + \delta T_j + \left(\theta \frac{\partial P_c}{\partial T_j} \right) \delta T_j + \left(\theta \frac{\partial P_c}{\partial T_j} \right)^2 \delta T_j + \cdots \tag{4.7}$$

The sum of this series will tend to infinity, i.e., thermal runaway will occur, if

$$\Theta \equiv \theta \frac{\partial P_c}{\partial T_j} \geqslant 1$$

For operation at the absolute limits of safety it is not advisable to let Θ exceed 0.5 with the worst possible combination of circuit parameters, supply voltage fluctuations, and component tolerances. If Θ is between 0 and -1, we observe that the sum (4.7) converges to a value between T_j and $T_j + \delta T_j$.

If the supply voltage is V_{cc} and the total resistance in the collector and emitter circuits is R, we have

$$P_c = i_c(V_{cc} - i_c R) \tag{4.8}$$

Hence for small changes in the collector current i_c,

$$\delta P_c = \delta i_c(V_{cc} - 2i_c R) \tag{4.9}$$

We can divide both sides of this equation by δT_j, and let δP_c, δi_c, and δT_j all tend to zero, to obtain

$$\frac{\partial P_c}{\partial T_j} = \frac{\partial i_c}{\partial T_j} (V_{cc} - 2i_c R) \tag{4.10}$$

Now $$V_{cc} = v_{ce} + i_c R$$

so we have finally

$$\theta \frac{\partial P_c}{\partial T_j} = \theta \frac{\partial i_c}{\partial T_j} (2v_{ce} - V_{cc}) \tag{4.11}$$

where the left-hand side is recognized as the quantity Θ which governs whether or not thermal runaway can occur. If the collector-emitter voltage v_{ce} is less than half the supply voltage V_{cc}, the right-hand side of this equation becomes negative, and thermal runaway is impossible. This is the *half supply voltage principle*. It is seen that the circuit of Fig. 4.14 conforms with this principle. The quantities θ and $\partial i_c / \partial T_j$ which appear in the right-hand side of equation (4.11) are always sufficiently small to rule out the possibility that the sum of the series (4.7) will oscillate infinitely!

It remains to calculate the input and output impedances and gain of the amplifier. The emitter of the transistor is short-circuited to earth from the point of view of an ac signal, so the input impedance is simply the base-emitter resistance, $r_{be} = \partial v_{be} / \partial i_b$, which is in the neighborhood of a thousand ohms. Here the shunting effect of the 10 k bias resistor could be taken into account if necessary. The output impedance consists of a 4.7 K resistor in parallel with the collector resistance, $\partial v_{ce} / \partial i_c$, whose value is estimated from the collector characteristics of Fig. 4.11 to be 40 K. Hence the output impedance is about 4.2 K. In order to calculate the voltage gain it is necessary to take into account the output impedance of the previous stage, as shown in Fig. 4.15.

The base current produced by the signal V_o is given as

$$di_b = \frac{dV_o}{r_{be} + Z_{out}} \tag{4.12}$$

The collector current $-\beta \, di_b$ flows through the collector load R_L, which in this case is 4.7 K. Hence the amplified signal is given by

$$dV_o' = -\beta R_L \frac{dV_o}{r_{be} + Z_{out}} \tag{4.13}$$

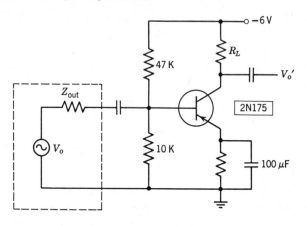

Fig. 4.15 Evaluation of voltage gain of amplifier.

and the voltage gain is $-\beta R_L/(r_{be} + Z_{out})$. In order for the amplification to be linear, it is necessary for Z_{out} to be somewhat larger than r_{be} so as to swamp the effect of the nonlinearity of the input characteristic (cf. Fig. 3.8). The current gain is seen to be $-\beta$, so the power gain is $\beta^2 R_L/(r_{be} + Z_{out})$.

Strictly speaking, we should also take account here of the finite collector resistance, $\partial v_{ce}/\partial i_c = r_c$, as with the plate resistance of a triode, and replace R_L in these formulas by $R_L r_c/(R_L + r_c)$. The current gain then becomes $\beta/(1 + R_L/r_c)$. The error involved in neglecting to do this is not very serious, especially in view of the large possible variation of β from one transistor to another, because r_c is normally much greater than R_L. A second omission, which can be important at high frequencies, is that we have neglected the internal capacitances of the transistor, notably those of the collector and emitter depletion layers. This point will be taken up again in Chapter 8. Finally, for a complete analysis the formulas should include a small term which results from the dependence of the input voltage v_{be} on the collector voltage v_{ce} at constant base current (Early effect). The complete analysis is usually carried out by making use of an *equivalent circuit* for the transistor, such as that (for the grounded-base configuration) shown in Fig. 4.16. In this circuit the "Early feedback" is represented by a voltage generator

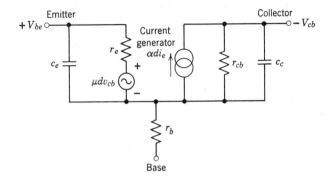

Fig. 4.16 T equivalent circuit for a transistor in the common-base configuration. Note: $r_{be} = r_b + r_e(1 + (3/\alpha) \sim r_b + r_e(1 + (3))$.

$\mu \, dv_{cb}$ in series with the emitter, and the signal is represented by a current generator $\alpha \, di_e$ in series with the load. Many more or less elaborate equivalent circuits for different transistor and vacuum tube configurations can be found in the references given at the end of the chapter. For most purposes the simplest approach, which we have used here, turns out to be quite adequate.

The last step remaining is to insert the actual numerical values. For the 2N175 the minimum value of β is listed as 65 (from a table given at end of the *GE Transistor Manual*), R_L is here equal to 4.7 K, r_{be} is approximately 1 K, and we suppose that Z_{out} is 3.3 K. Hence the voltage gain is -70, the current gain is -65, and the power gain is 4.2×10^3. The power gain is usually stated in decibels (gain in decibels $= 10 \times \log$ [gain] to base 10): in this example it comes to 36 decibels. These values will all be affected by the input impedance of the following stage, which will act as a shunt across the 4.7 K load resistor. If we wish to avoid this effect, it can be overcome either by means of transformer coupling to the next stage, as in Fig. 4.17, or by making use of the high input impedance and low output impedance of an intermediate emitter-follower stage, which is then said to function as an *impedance transformer*. For laboratory work an emitter follower is normally more convenient to use than a bulky transformer, which may have to be specially wound and will in any case have a limited frequency response, although interstage

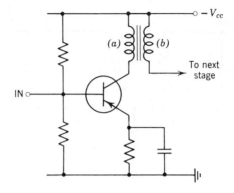

Fig. 4.17 Transformer coupling: (*a*) high-impedance winding, (*b*) low-impedance winding.

transformers are very commonly used in power amplifiers, where impedance matching is particularly important.[3]

4d GROUNDED-GRID AMPLIFIER

The basic circuit for a grounded-grid amplifier is shown in Fig. 4.18. Apart from providing a form of amplifier with low input and high output impedance, the grounded-grid configuration has the important property that the earthed control grid acts as a very effective screen between the input and output circuits. Thus a grounded-grid amplifier can be used at higher frequencies than the

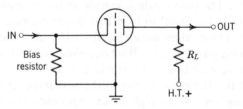

Fig. 4.18 Grounded-grid amplifier.

[3] The *impedance ratio* of a transformer is equal to the square of the *turns ratio*, which is effectively the same as the *voltage ratio*. Hence the use of a voltage step-down transformer in Fig. 4.17 for impedance matching is not such a disadvantage as it might seem.

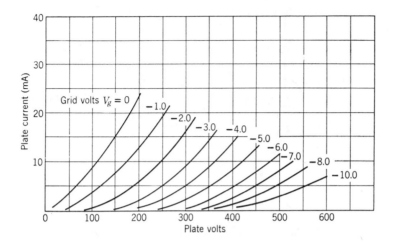

Fig. 4.19   Plate characteristics, 12AT7 triode section.

corresponding common-cathode amplifier without special precautions to reduce the effects of interaction between input and output.   In this type of application the cathode and anode loads are usually in the form of resonant circuits (section 1c), so we can assume that the loads are purely resistive, as will be the case at the resonant frequency.

The tube to be used as an example of a grounded-grid amplifier is an RCA type 6AB4, which is a high-mu triode ($\mu = 60$) having a 6.3 V heater.   Two of these triodes are contained in the same envelope in an RCA type 12AT7 (Mullard ECC81).   The plate characteristics are given in Fig. 4.19.

The supply voltage will be assumed to be $+250$ V.   The maximum-rated anode voltage is $+300$ V, and the maximum-rated plate dissipation is 2.5 W, corresponding to a current of 10 mA at 250 V. The chosen operating point is at a plate current of 5 mA, with the grid 1 V negative with respect to the cathode, and an anode potential of $+120$ V.   The maximum input signal is assumed to be 1 V peak to peak, which can be exceeded by a factor of 2 before running into the grid current region.   There are two easy methods of obtaining the correct grid bias relative to the cathode, as shown in Figs. 4.20a and 4.20b.

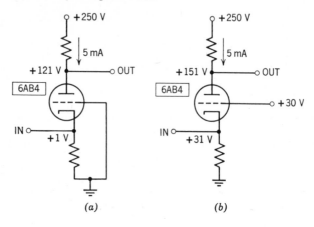

Fig. 4.20   Biasing of grounded-grid amplifier.

The simplest self-bias method (Fig. 4.20*a*) has the disadvantage that the cathode resistor works out to be only 220 ohms, so that a large proportion of the input signal will flow through it to earth in preference to flowing through the tube, and the current gain of the stage will be very much smaller than 1. The second method (Fig. 4.20*b*) does not suffer to the same extent from this disadvantage because the cathode resistor now works out to be 6.2 K. The +30 V for the grid can be obtained from a simple potential divider, with a capacitor between the grid and earth so that it is effectively grounded from the point of view of an ac signal. This capacitor can be quite small if we are working at moderately high frequencies. The resulting circuit is shown in Fig. 4.21. The method of coupling to other stages will depend on the nature of the application and does not need to be specified here.

To calculate the gain and input impedance of this amplifier we use the general formula

$$di_a = \frac{dv_a}{\rho} + g_m \, dv_g \qquad (4.1)$$

where the input signal is now

$$dv_{in} = dv_k = -dv_g \qquad (4.14)$$

(the subscript k refers to the cathode). Now since

$$dv_{\text{out}} = -R_L\, di_a \tag{4.15}$$

and

$$dv_a = dv_{\text{out}} - dv_{\text{in}}$$

we obtain as the expression for the gain

$$\frac{dv_{\text{out}}}{dv_{\text{in}}} = \frac{g_m\rho R_L + R_L}{R_L + \rho}$$

$$= \frac{(\mu + 1)R_L}{R_L + \rho} \tag{4.16}$$

This expression is positive, which indicates that the input and output signals are in phase. Using $\mu = 60$, $R_L = 22$ K, and $\rho = 14$ K, we find the voltage gain to be $+37$.

The input impedance is provided by $\partial v_k / \partial i_a$ for the tube, in parallel with the 6.8 K cathode resistor. From (4.15) and (4.16)

$$\frac{dv_k}{di_a} = -\frac{R_L + \rho}{\mu + 1} \tag{4.17}$$

$$= -550 \text{ ohms}$$

This comes out negative because a positive input signal causes i_a to decrease; i.e., $+di_a$ from the point of view of the incoming signal

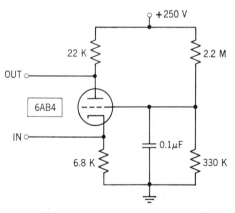

Fig. 4.21 Final grounded-grid stage.

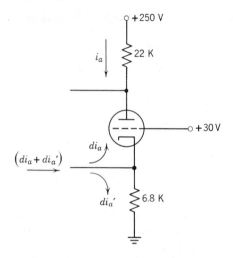

Fig. 4.22   Path of signal current in a
grounded-grid stage.

is $-di_a$ from the point of view of the tube (Fig. 4.22).   Therefore the input impedance is simply equal to 550 ohms and 6.8 K in parallel, i.e., 507 ohms.

The output impedance consists of the 22 K load resistor in parallel with the 14 K plate resistance of the tube, which works out to be 8.5 K.   The current gain of the stage is appreciably less than one because a fraction of the input current flows to earth via the cathode and anode resistors.   If these resistors are actually the windings of ideal interstage transformers, a current gain of unity can be achieved.

4e   TRANSISTOR COMMON-BASE AMPLIFIER

As would be expected, this amplifier is rather like the one we have just discussed.   In an amplifier composed entirely of transistors in the common-base configuration, the only reasonable method of interstage coupling is by means of transformers, and the problem of designing a high-frequency amplifier becomes one of designing suitable transformers (assuming that the transistors have been chosen to have a sufficiently high value of the α-cutoff frequency f_α).   The obvious alternative, of driving the grounded-base amplifier from the low output impedance of an emitter-follower stage, gives rise to a new circuit, the "long-tailed pair," which is described in Chapter 5. With a given transistor the cutoff frequency in the grounded-base configuration is much higher than in the grounded-emitter or emitter-follower configurations.

An example of a grounded-base stage is shown in Fig. 4.23, using a Mullard OC45 transistor (average $\beta = 50$, $f_\alpha = 6$ Mc/sec, maximum $i_c = 5$ mA, maximum $v_{cb} = -10$ V). The reader should verify that at the chosen operating point the collector current is 2 mA, the base current is 0.04 mA, the collector potential is -2 V, and thermal runaway cannot occur.

To calculate the impedances and the gain of the amplifier we use the expressions

$$di_c = \beta\, di_b = \alpha\, di_e \tag{4.18}$$

$$dv_{\text{in}} = dv_e = -dv_{be} \tag{4.19}$$

$$dv_{be} = -r_{be}\, di_b \tag{4.20}$$

and
$$dv_c = dv_{\text{out}} = +R_L\, di_c \tag{4.21}$$

Here we are neglecting $r_{cb} = \partial v_{cb}/\partial i_c$ which is effectively in parallel with R_L.

The input impedance is provided by dv_e/di_e in parallel with the 3.3 K emitter resistor. From the preceding equations

$$\frac{dv_e}{di_e} = \frac{\alpha r_{be}}{\beta} = (1 - \alpha)r_{be} = Z_{\text{in}} \tag{4.22}$$

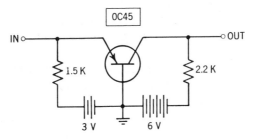

Fig. 4.23 Common-base amplifier stage.

From the slope of the input characteristic at the operating point, r_{be} is found to be about 1.1 K, β is known to be 50, and α is therefore 0.98. Hence

$$\frac{dv_e}{di_e} = 22 \text{ ohms}$$

and the 1.5 K emitter resistor can be neglected. The current gain is seen to be very slightly less than α, i.e., about 0.97. The voltage gain is

$$\frac{dv_c}{dv_e} = \frac{R_L\beta}{r_{be}} \sim \frac{\alpha Z_{\text{out}}}{Z_{\text{in}}} \tag{4.23}$$

$$= 100$$

The power gain is therefore 20 decibels. The output impedance is provided by the 2.2 K load in parallel with the collector resistance, which is found from the common-base output characteristics to be 2 M. In this case, however, the Early feedback has a significant effect (cf. Fig. 4.16) and it can be shown that the output impedance *of the transistor* is in fact given by the formula

$$Z_{\text{out}} = \frac{r_{cb}(r_e + Z'_{\text{out}})}{\mu r_{cb}/\alpha + Z'_{\text{out}} + r_e}$$

where Z'_{out} is the output impedance of the signal source. For the OC45 we have $\mu = 3.8 \times 10^{-4}$, $r_e = 25$ ohms, $\alpha = 0.98$, and $r_{cb} = 2$ M. Thus if we assume $Z'_{\text{out}} = 100$ ohms, we find

$$Z_{\text{out}} = 300 \text{ K} \sim \frac{\alpha Z'_{\text{out}}}{\mu}$$

Hence the net output impedance is still 2.2 K. A higher gain and higher output impedance could be obtained with the same voltage source by increasing the collector and emitter loads, but this would involve moving from a fairly linear part of the input characteristic to a region of very pronounced curvature (Fig. 4.24). A better procedure would be to increase both the collector load and the voltage of the battery in the collector circuit. A common-base stage can readily be constructed to have a voltage gain in excess of 1000, but it becomes difficult to make use of all this gain because of the extremely high output impedance which results.

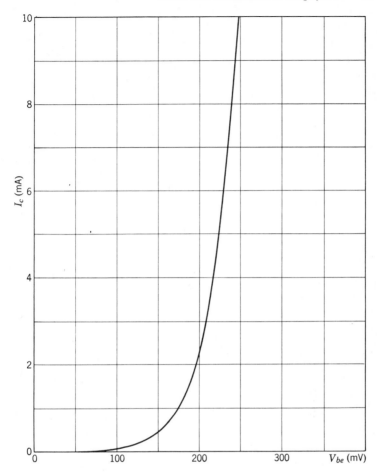

Fig. 4.24 Collector current versus base-emitter voltage for OC45 transistor.

4f THE CATHODE FOLLOWER

The essential features of a cathode-follower stage are shown in Fig. 4.25. To analyze this circuit we again use the general equation

$$di_a = \frac{dv_a}{\rho} + g_m \, dv_g \qquad (4.1)$$

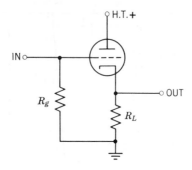

Fig. 4.25   Cathode follower.

where in the present case

$$dv_a = -dv_{out} \qquad (4.24)$$

$$dv_g = dv_{in} - dv_{out} \qquad (4.25)$$

and

$$dv_{out} = R_L \, di_a \qquad (4.26)$$

Therefore equation (4.1) becomes

$$\rho \, di_a = -(1 + \mu) \, dv_{out} + \mu \, dv_{in} \qquad (4.27)$$

The voltage gain is given by

$$\frac{dv_{out}}{dv_{in}} = \frac{\mu}{\mu + 1 + \rho/R_L} \sim \frac{\mu}{\mu + 1} \qquad (4.28)$$

where $\mu \gg 1 \sim \rho/R_L$, and so the voltage gain is close to unity. To put this into words, the cathode potential accurately follows any fluctuation of the grid potential—hence the name cathode follower.

The input impedance is simply R_g, which can be made very large indeed (up to 10^{15} ohms). The output impedance is given by $\partial v_{out}/\partial i_a$ (at constant input voltage[4]) in parallel with R_L. Putting $dv_i = 0$ in (4.27), we find

$$\left(\frac{\partial v_{out}}{\partial i_a} \right)_{v_{in}} = -\frac{\rho}{1 + \mu} \sim -\frac{1}{g_m} \qquad (4.29)$$

where the negative sign merely signifies that i_a decreases when v_{out} increases, and can be disregarded when we insert numerical values.

[4] The requirement of constant input voltage results from Thevenin's theorem. Cf. section 4a, Fig. 4.2a, and reference 3 (list at end of chapter), section 1.7.

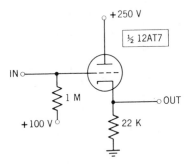

Fig. 4.26   Practical cathode follower.

A practical cathode-follower stage is shown in Fig. 4.26.   The tube that is employed here is one section of a 12AT7 double triode (cf. Fig. 4.19).   At the chosen operating point the anode current is 4.5 mA and the grid is about 1.5 V negative with respect to the cathode.

In this example $\mu = 60$, $R_L = 22$ K, ρ is approximately 14 K, and g_m is 4.2×10^{-3} ohm^{-1}.   Hence the input impedance is 1 M, the output impedance is 240 ohms, and the voltage gain is 0.97.

4g   THE EMITTER FOLLOWER

A typical emitter-follower stage is shown in Fig. 4.27.   This particular example uses any transistor with $\beta \sim 50$ and maximum ratings in the neighborhood of $i_c = 10$ mA and $v_{ce} = -10$ V (or greater).   The collector current at the chosen operating point is 3 mA.

Here the signal current in the base is given by

$$di_b = -\frac{dv_{be}}{r_{be}} \tag{4.30}$$

where
$$dv_{be} = dv_{\text{in}} - dv_{\text{out}} \tag{4.31}$$

and
$$dv_{\text{out}} = -di_e R_L \tag{4.32}$$

Also
$$\alpha \, di_e = di_c = \beta \, di_b \tag{4.33}$$

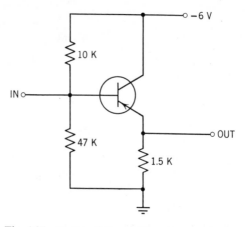

Fig. 4.27   Emitter follower ($\beta = 50$, $i_c = 3$ mA).

From (4.30) and (4.31)

$$dv_{\text{in}} - dv_{\text{out}} = -di_b r_{be}$$

and

$$= -\alpha \, di_e \frac{r_{be}}{\beta} \qquad \text{from (4.33)}$$

$$= \frac{+\alpha r_{be} \, dv_{\text{out}}}{R_L \beta} \qquad \text{from (4.32)}$$

Hence the voltage gain is

$$\frac{dv_{\text{out}}}{dv_{\text{in}}} = \left(1 + \frac{\alpha r_{be}}{\beta R_L}\right)^{-1} \qquad (4.34)$$

which is close to unity, since $\beta \gg \alpha$ and $R_L \sim r_{be}$. In the present example the voltage gain works out to be 0.98, assuming that r_{be} is about 1.5 K.

Further manipulation of equations (4.30) to (4.33) yields for the input impedance of the transistor

$$\frac{dv_{\text{in}}}{di_b} = -\left(r_{be} + \frac{\beta R_L}{\alpha}\right) \qquad (4.35)$$

where the negative sign signifies that when the input voltage increment is positive, the base current decreases. In the present case the expression on the right-hand side of (4.35) works out to be 77 K, so in fact the input impedance of the circuit is decided mainly by the

10 K biasing resistor. This circuit would therefore be considerably improved by increasing the supply voltage to -9 V, and increasing the smaller biasing resistor from 10 K to 39 K or even 47 K. If the transistor possessed a higher voltage rating than -10 V, this sort of improvement could be carried still further. (Transistors with maximum voltage ratings of up to 200 V are available at present, but those with high voltage ratings tend to be rather expensive.) The output impedance with $dv_{in} = 0$ is given by

$$\frac{dv_{out}}{di_e} = \frac{\alpha r_{be}}{\beta} \tag{4.36}$$

which here works out to be 30 ohms. (This is in parallel with R_L.)

In a practical case it would be necessary to include in these formulas the output impedance of the previous stage in series with r_{be}, and the input impedance of the following stage in parallel with R_L.

EXERCISES

4.1 A battery with an internal resistance R_o ohms and e.m.f. E_o volts is used to drive a current through a heating coil of resistance R. Show that the power P which is dissipated in the heater is $E_o^2 R/(R + R_o)^2$, and (by putting $dP/dR = 0$) that this is a maximum when $R = R_o$ (*maximum power theorem*).

4.2 Assign suitable wattage ratings to the resistors which are shown in Figs. 4.21, 4.23, 4.26, and 4.27.

4.3 Deduce as much as you can about the operating points of the tubes which appear in the following circuits.

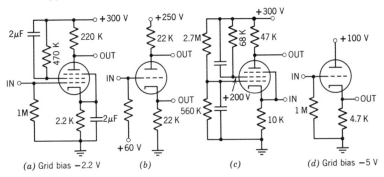

(a) Grid bias -2.2 V   (b)   (c)   (d) Grid bias -5 V

Ex. 4.3

4.4 Deduce as much as you can about the operating points of the transistors which appear in the following circuits.

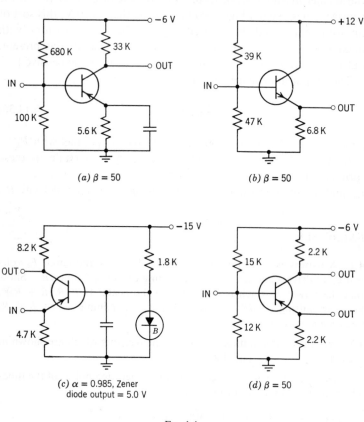

(a) $\beta = 50$

(b) $\beta = 50$

(c) $\alpha = 0.985$, Zener
diode output = 5.0 V

(d) $\beta = 50$

Ex. 4.4

4.5 Design a common-cathode amplifier using a 6AB4 triode and compare its properties with those of the pentode amplifier of section 4b.

4.6 Design a cathode follower using a 6AU6 pentode and compare its properties with those of the circuit shown in Fig. 4.26. (Note that in the configuration which results the tube is said to be *triode-connected*.)

4.7 Each of the circuits in Exercise 4.4 is driven from a voltage generator having an output impedance of 5 K. Evaluate $\partial V_{\text{out}}/\partial V_{\text{in}}$ and the output impedance in each case.

4.8 The base-emitter voltage of a transistor, v_{be}, decreases by about 2 mV per degree centigrade, at a given base current. What would be the advantage of inserting a forward-biased diode in series with one of the biasing resistors, as shown below?

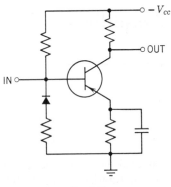

Ex. 4.8

REFERENCES

1. W. H. Aldous and E. Appleton, *Thermionic vacuum tubes.* London: Methuen & Co., Sixth Edition, 1952, Chapter VI.
2. *Mullard reference manual of transistor circuits.* London: Mullard, Ltd., 1960, Chapters 5, 7, and 12.
3. H. A. Romanowitz. *Fundamentals of semiconductor and tube electronics.* New York: John Wiley & Sons, Inc., 1962, Chapters 1 and 9.
4. *RCA receiving tube manual.* Harrison, N.J.: Radio Corporation of America, 1964.
5. *RCA transistor manual.* Somerville, N.J.: Radio Corporation of America, 1962.
6. *GE transistor manual.* Syracuse, N.Y.: General Electric Company, Sixth Edition, 1962.
7. *Mullard technical handbook*, Volume 4. London: Mullard, Ltd., 1964.

5

Multistage Amplifiers

....

5a INTRODUCTION

In Chapter 4 we considered the basic types of amplifier stage which use only a single tube or transistor. In this chapter we begin by describing some useful amplifiers which contain two active elements, namely the long-tailed pair, the Darlington amplifier, and the cascode amplifier. Each of these circuits constitutes an ingenious method of connecting two tubes or transistors together in order to obtain the equivalent of a single stage with especially desirable properties. After describing these circuits we discuss the advantages that can be obtained, and some of the problems that arise, from connecting a number of amplifier stages in series. These topics will lead in turn to discussions of power amplifiers and of dc amplifiers and electrometers. We do not exhaust the subject of amplifiers in this chapter, for we shall return to it in Chapter 7, under the heading of "feedback," where we describe the use of negative feedback to produce amplifiers having stable gain and controlled frequency response, and in Chapter 8, where we discuss general questions of gain, bandwidth, and amplifier noise.

5b SOME SPECIAL AMPLIFIER CONFIGURATIONS

The Long-Tailed Pair. As shown in Fig. 5.1, this circuit can be constructed with either tubes or transistors. It has the useful property that the output is proportional to the difference between the two input signals, rather than to the actual magnitudes of these signals. Alternatively, if one input is grounded for alternating current, a signal applied to the other input is converted into two equal out-of-phase signals at the output, i.e., the circuit can function as a *phase splitter*. A third application, to be described later, arises from the fact that in transistor amplifiers for dc signals the temperature variation of the base-emitter voltage v_{be} gives rise to unwanted drifts in the output. If the two transistors of the long-tailed pair are identical and are subject to the same temperature variations, each output will be affected equally by the changes in v_{be}, and this source of drift will have been eliminated. The circuit also finds frequent application in dc amplifiers using vacuum tubes. The long-tailed pair can be regarded as a combination of a cathode or emitter follower with a grounded-grid or grounded-base amplifier, where the low output impedance of the one is matched by the low input impedance of the other.

In our analysis of this circuit we shall assume that one of the two input terminals is grounded from the point of view of alternating current. For the tube amplifier we can write, using the same symbols as in Chapter 4, and assuming the two tubes 1 and 2 to be identical,

$$di_1 = \frac{dv_1}{\rho} + g_m \, dv_{g1} \tag{5.1}$$

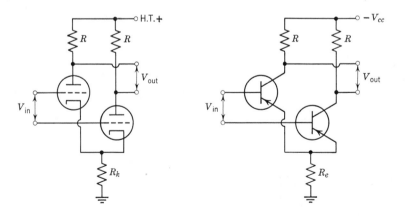

Fig. 5.1 Long-tailed pair.

and
$$di_2 = \frac{dv_2}{\rho} + g_m \, dv_{g2} \tag{5.2}$$

where
$$dv_1 = -di_1 R \tag{5.3}$$

$$dv_2 = -di_2 R \tag{5.4}$$

$$dv_{g1} = dv_{in} - R_k(di_1 + di_2) \tag{5.5}$$

and
$$dv_{g2} = -R_k(di_1 + di_2) \tag{5.6}$$

Hence, eliminating di_1, di_2, dv_{g1}, and dv_{g2} from equations (5.1) and (5.2), we find

$$dv_1\left(\frac{g_m R_k}{R} - \frac{1}{R} - \frac{1}{\rho}\right) + dv_2 \frac{g_m R_k}{R} = g_m \, dv_{in} \tag{5.7}$$

and
$$dv_2\left(\frac{g_m R_k}{R} - \frac{1}{R} - \frac{1}{\rho}\right) + dv_1 \frac{g_m R_k}{R} = 0 \tag{5.8}$$

Now suppose that R_k, R, and ρ are all about equal. Then, since $g_m\rho = \mu \gg 1$, equation (5.8) becomes simply

$$dv_1 = -dv_2 \tag{5.9}$$

and the circuit functions as a phase splitter. The effect of the terms $1/R$ and $1/\rho$ in (5.8), plus any small inherent differences between the tubes, can be compensated for by introducing a potentiometer adjustment for the two anode loads, as in Fig. 5.2, where some

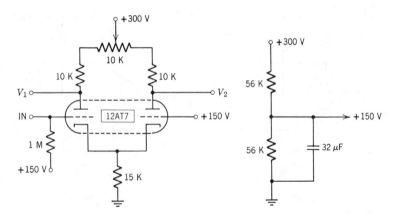

Fig. 5.2   Practical long-tailed pair circuit using a 12AT7 double triode.

typical component values are specified. From equations (5.7) and (5.8) we have

$$(dv_2 - dv_1)\frac{R + \rho}{R\rho} = g_m\,dv_{\text{in}} \qquad (5.10)$$

Hence, by using (5.9),

$$-\frac{dv_1}{dv_{\text{in}}} = \frac{dv_2}{dv_{\text{in}}} = \frac{g_m R\rho}{2(R + \rho)} \qquad (5.11)$$

For the components shown in Fig. 5.2 the gain to each output works out to be ± 16, or -32 in terms of $(dv_1 - dv_2)/dv_{\text{in}}$.

A practical example of the analogous transistor circuit is shown in Fig. 5.3. The two transistors have $\beta = 45$, v_{ce} maximum $= -16$ V, and i_c maximum $= 15$ mA. Here essentially the same considerations apply as with tubes, since the response of the transistors to voltage changes will be linear provided the output impedance of the previous stage, Z_{out}, is sufficiently greater than the nonlinear base input resistance r_{be}. The calculation of the relationships between the input and output signals is left as an exercise for the reader (Exercise 5.4).

The Darlington Configuration. The Darlington amplifier (Fig. 5.4) can be regarded as a combination of two emitter-follower stages in series, with the input impedance of the second stage acting as the load impedance for the first. The current gain for the whole amplifier

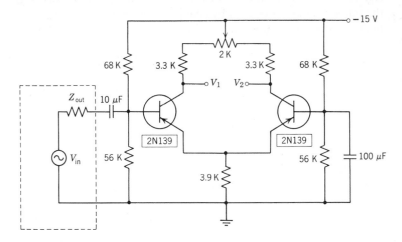

Fig. 5.3 Practical long-tailed pair using transistors.

is seen to be $\beta_1\beta_2$, and all the emitter current of the first transistor flows through the base of the second. This implies that the second transistor is somewhat larger than the first in terms of current-carrying capacity.

From the results of section 4g, the output impedance of the first transistor is $\alpha_1(Z_{\text{out}} + r_{be1})/\beta_1$. This is in series with r_{be2} at the input of the second transistor, so that the final output impedance is given by $\alpha_2[r_{be2} + \alpha_1(Z_{\text{out}} + r_{be1})/\beta_1]/\beta_2$. If Z_{out} is very large, as is often the case, this reduces to $\alpha_1\alpha_2 Z_{\text{out}}/\beta_1\beta_2$.

The input impedance at the second transistor is equal to $-(r_{be2} + \beta_2 R_L/\alpha_2)$, where r_{be2} is generally much smaller than $\beta_2 R_L/\alpha_2$, and the negative sign can be ignored if we remember that the base current decreases when the input voltage swings positive. The load for the first transistor is then $\beta_2 R_L/\alpha_2$, so that the input impedance of the first transistor becomes $-(r_{be1} + \beta_1\beta_2 R_L/\alpha_1\alpha_2)$, or $\beta_1\beta_2 R_L/\alpha_1\alpha_2$ to a very good approximation.

In effect, the Darlington configuration is therefore equivalent to a single transistor having $\alpha = \alpha_1\alpha_2$, $\beta = \beta_1\beta_2$, $r_{be} = r_{be1}$, and $v_{be} = v_{be1} + v_{be2}$. A minor disadvantage of this configuration is that the leakage current of the first transistor contributes to the base current of the second, so that if several transistors are to be connected together in this way, the first ones in line should always be low-leakage silicon transistors. A second disadvantage is that drifts in the output voltage produced by changes of v_{be} with temperature are multiplied by the number of transistors in the line.

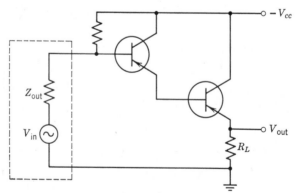

Fig. 5.4   The Darlington configuration.

The Cascode Amplifier. In the cascode amplifier (Fig. 5.5) two triodes are connected together in such a way so that one forms the anode load of the other. For the bottom section we have

$$di = \frac{dv_a}{\rho} + g_m \, dv_{\text{in}} \tag{5.12}$$

and for the top section

$$di = \frac{dv_{\text{out}}}{\rho} - g_m \, dv_a \tag{5.13}$$

where

$$dv_{\text{out}} = -R_L \, di \tag{5.14}$$

From (5.13) and (5.14)

$$dv_a = \frac{dv_{\text{out}}(1/R_L + 1/\rho)}{g_m} \tag{5.15}$$

and from (5.12) and (5.15)

$$di = \frac{dv_{\text{out}}(R + \rho)}{g_m \rho^2 R} + g_m \, dv_{\text{in}} \tag{5.16}$$

Thus the cascode amplifier is equivalent to a single tube of transconductance g_m, of plate resistance $\rho\mu R/(R + \rho)$, and of amplification factor $\mu^2 R/(R + \rho)$, where $\mu = g_m \rho$ is the amplification

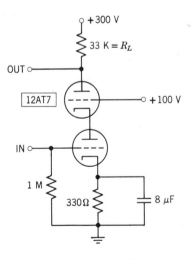

Fig. 5.5 A cascode amplifier stage.

factor for one of the triodes alone. These values would be fairly typical of a high-gain pentode. For the circuit of Fig. 5.5, $g_m = 4.2 \times 10^{-3}$ ohm^{-1}, $\rho = 14$ K, $\mu = 60$, and the overall voltage gain works out to be -140. A cascode amplifier is sometimes to be preferred to the equivalent pentode stage because of its lower noise figure and slightly better high-frequency response (see Chapter 8). It is also a useful constant-current source (see Chapter 7).

5c AMPLIFIERS WITH CASCADED STAGES

Vacuum tube amplifiers with more than one stage are very often coupled through capacitors, as shown in Fig. 5.6. This method works well, since the input impedance of each stage is high and the voltage gain of the preceding stage can be fully utilized. The coupling capacitors must be large enough to provide negligible attenuation of the low-frequency components of the signals which are to be transmitted (cf. the differentiating network, Chapter 1). It is not usually advisable to attempt to build a voltage amplifier with more than three or four stages on a single chassis, because it becomes too easy for some of the output to return to the input as "positive feedback" and cause oscillations to build up. To help prevent unwanted interactions over one or two stages, the anode supplies to successive tubes are "decoupled" from one another, as in Fig. 5.6,

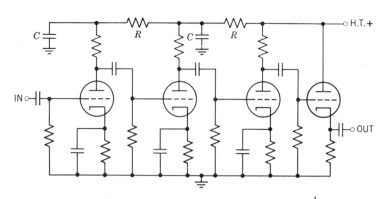

Fig. 5.6. Multistage amplifier with coupling through interstage capacitors.

by means of *RC* filter networks. (Typically, $R = 5$ K, $C = 8$ μF.) The last stage of an amplifier is usually made a cathode follower in order to match the impedance of any following circuit, charge stray capacitances in connecting cables, and so on. The use of negative feedback to stabilize the gain of multistage amplifiers is described in Chapter 7.

Transistor amplifiers can also be cascaded by way of coupling capacitors, as in Fig. 5.7, but there is then a considerable loss of voltage gain because the low input impedance of the second stage acts as a shunt across the load of the first stage. To make best use of the capabilities of common-emitter stages in series it is necessary to use transformer coupling, or intermediate emitter-follower stages, as mentioned in section 4c.

To illustrate these statements let us calculate the overall gain of the two-stage amplifier in Fig. 5.7. The resistor R, which is inserted to overcome the nonlinearity of the input characteristic of transistor 2, is assumed to be of similar magnitude to Z_{out} of the previous circuit, and both of these are assumed to be much less than R_L. Omitting resistor R would not affect the validity of the argument which follows.

For the first stage alone the voltage gain would be $-\beta R_L/(r_{be}+Z_{out})$. In the presence of the second stage the load resistor R_L is shunted by $R + r_{be}$, so that the voltage gain of the first stage is reduced to $-\beta(R + r_{be})/(r_{be} + Z_{out})$, or $-\beta$, approximately. The effective voltage gain of the second stage is $-\beta R_L/(R + r_{be})$, so that the overall voltage gain is $\beta^2 R_L/(R + r_{be})$, and the current gain is β^2. Hence

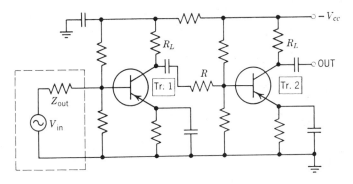

Fig. 5.7 Effect of cascading common-emitter stages.

there is little advantage in using a common-emitter first stage, rather than, say, an emitter follower with the same value of R_L, because only the current gain of the transistor is effective. This is not true with transformer coupling because the action of the step-down transformer that is required for proper impedance matching converts the first-stage voltage gain into additional current gain, with very little loss in terms of the overall *power* gain. In practice the choice between common emitter and emitter follower for the input stage is governed by whether the output impedance of the signal source is low or high.

Small-signal amplifiers may also be coupled directly, as in Fig. 5.8. An amplifier of this type will respond to low-frequency signals and, if the bypass capacitors on the cathode resistors are removed, can even be used as a *dc amplifier*, for magnifying small changes in dc voltage levels. The design of dc amplifiers involves a number of interesting problems, especially if the small changes of dc level occur in high-impedance circuits, and since such amplifiers have many applications in research, they are thought to merit a separate discussion in section 5d.

Power amplifiers also present special problems, arising mainly from the fact that for economic reasons it is important to convert as much as possible of the power which is delivered by the voltage supply into usable output signal. This almost invariably involves trans-former coupling in order to achieve correct impedance matching.

A graphical method of estimating the performance of an amplifier stage, which is especially valuable in the design of power amplifiers but

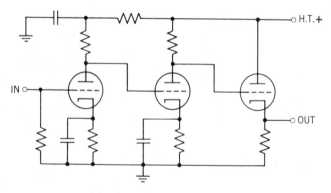

Fig. 5.8   Direct-coupled amplifier.

can also be very useful for amplifiers in general, is illustrated in Fig. 5.9. The method consists of drawing the *load line,*

$$v_a = v_{\text{supply}} - i_a R_L \qquad (5.17)$$

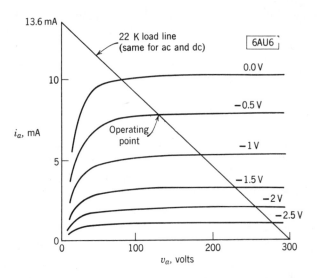

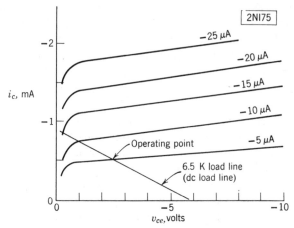

Fig. 5.9 Load lines for the 6AU6 and 2N175 amplifiers of Chapter 4. Note that with the 2N175 the ac load line would cut the *x* axis at $v_{ce} = 5.1$ V and pass through the same operating point as the dc load line.

for a tube, or

$$v_{ce} = v_{cc} - i_c R_L \qquad (5.18)$$

for a transistor.[1]

The load line intersects the horizontal axis at the value of the supply voltage, and the vertical axis at the value of the current that would flow if the whole supply voltage were connected across the load resistor R_L. The operating point is fixed by the intersection of the load line with the characteristic curve which corresponds to the chosen value of grid voltage or base current. As the grid voltage or base current varies in the presence of an incoming signal, the operating point moves backwards and forwards along the load line in such a way that it always occupies the intersection of the load line with the characteristic that corresponds to the instantaneous value of grid voltage or base current. Useful information can be extracted from these diagrams as follows:

1.   The voltage gain of the amplifier can be estimated from the relative sizes of the change in anode or collector voltage and the corresponding change in grid voltage or base current when the operating point moves a short distance along the load line.

2.   The size of an incoming signal which will produce distortion of the output can be estimated by noting where the load line begins to intersect the characteristics in their nonlinear regions.

3.   The likelihood that the tube or transistor will exceed its permissible plate or collector dissipation can be estimated by observing how close the load line comes to the boundary of the allowed operating region (often shown as a dashed hyperbola superimposed upon the characteristics).

4.   The best conditions for operating a tube or transistor as a power amplifier can be found by selecting a load line for optimum values of voltage swing and current swing with a given input signal, combined with minimum distortion. (Usually the requirement of low distortion causes the optimum load to be two or three times the plate resistance of a triode, rather than equal to the plate resistance, as would be expected from the maximum power theorem.)

---

[1] These are the load lines for the common-cathode and common-emitter configurations. For load lines for other amplifier configurations see Exercise 5.2.

Since in a power amplifier the aim is to convert as much as possible of the supply power into output, it is apparent that an ordinary amplifier in Class A operation, i.e., under conditions where there is always some unmodulated anode or collector current flowing, is not achieving maximum efficiency. With ideal characteristics, such that the current falls just to zero once in each cycle and the anode or collector voltage falls to zero at maximum current, the theoretical efficiency is 50%. If two stages are used in *push-pull* (Fig. 5.10) in such a way that each stage conducts during exactly one-half of a cycle (Class B operation), the theoretical maximum efficiency rises

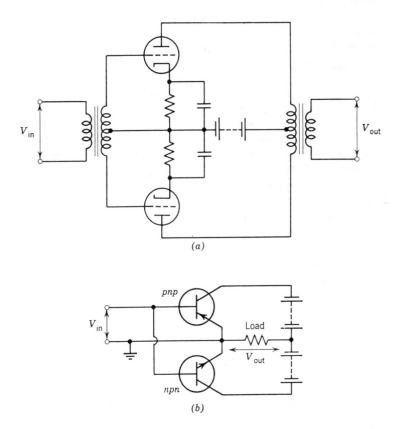

Fig. 5.10 Push-pull amplifiers: (*a*) using identical tubes, (*b*) using transistors with complementary symmetry.

to 78.5%. With transistors some advantage can be gained here from making use of complementary symmetry, i.e., by using two transistors which are identical except that one is *pnp* and the other *npn*. In Class C operation, each stage being cut off for more than half a cycle so that the current flows only in brief pulses, the theoretical maximum efficiency approaches 100% and practical efficiencies of 60 to 80% are attainable. This mode of operation is only feasible if the signal is in the form of a high-frequency carrier wave, with the information that is being carried impressed as relatively low-frequency modulation of the carrier, as in a radio transmission. Because of the distortion that results from passing only short current pulses, it is necessary to have a tuned circuit in the output to select the desired frequency and reject the various harmonics which are present. Alternatively, the tuned circuit can be designed to resonate at the frequency of one of the harmonics, so that a Class C amplifier can be employed as a frequency doubler or trebler.

The topics which have been discussed in this section are sufficiently diverse to make a summary worth while. The main points are:

1. Voltage amplifiers using vacuum tubes can usefully be con- nected in series, with multiplication of the separate voltage gains. The number of stages which may be connected together in one unit is limited by the likelihood of instability from unintentional positive feedback.

2. There is considerable loss of voltage gain on simply cascading transistor common-emitter stages. To overcome this, transformer coupling, or the use of intermediate emitter-follower stages, is recommended.

3. Much useful information about the performance of an amplifier stage can be obtained by drawing appropriate load lines on the output characteristics of the tube or transistor.

4. The efficiency of power amplifiers can be improved by the use of push-pull configurations and Class B or Class C operation, in which the tube or transistor is cut off for 50% or more of the time.

5d DIRECT-CURRENT AMPLIFIERS AND ELECTROMETERS

Direct-current amplifiers, by definition, respond to signals at frequencies that range right down to zero. Usually the amplifier response is also maintained at audio frequencies, and sometimes even higher. A dc amplifier which can be used to measure voltage changes in very high impedance circuits (10^8 ohms and above) is termed an *electrometer*, and special precautions are required in order to secure the necessary high input impedance. These precautions normally affect only the input stage of the amplifier, so we shall begin by considering dc amplifiers in general. Ordinary dc amplifiers commonly form a part of temperature-measuring devices using thermocouples, thermistors, or resistance thermometers, of automatic control systems and servo systems, and of various types of measuring instruments in which the incorporation of a dc amplifier enables a robust panel meter to be used in place of a delicate galvanometer. Electrometer amplifiers find application in pH measurements with the glass electrode, in flame ionization detectors for gas chromatography, in mass spectrometers (for measuring ion currents), in ionization gauges for measuring gas pressures below 10^{-3} torr, in certain types of photometer, and in various kinds of measurement with ionization chambers.

Since capacitors and transformers do not convey signals at very low frequencies, it is apparent that amplifiers for direct current must be direct-coupled, as is the vacuum tube amplifier of Fig. 5.11.

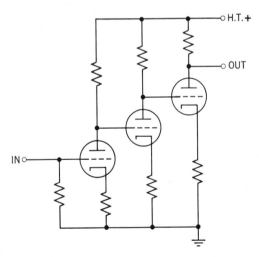

Fig. 5.11 First attempt at a dc amplifier.

As it stands this circuit has one or two obvious flaws.   The first is that the potential of the output rises higher and higher as more stages are added, because the grid voltage of each stage has to be the same as the anode voltage of the previous one.   The second flaw, which is really a consequence of the first, is that the unbypassed cathode resistors become steadily larger and larger in comparison with the anode loads, and, because of cathode-follower action, the gain per stage therefore becomes steadily smaller (cf. Exercise 5.3).

To reduce the voltage level at the input of a succeeding stage, it is possible to use a simple voltage divider, as in Fig. 5.12*a*, a neon glow tube as in Fig. 5.12*b*, or a Zener diode as in Fig. 5.12*c*.   A moderate reduction in the voltage level can also be secured by inserting a small battery, as in Fig. 5.12*d*.   Each of the first three methods involves

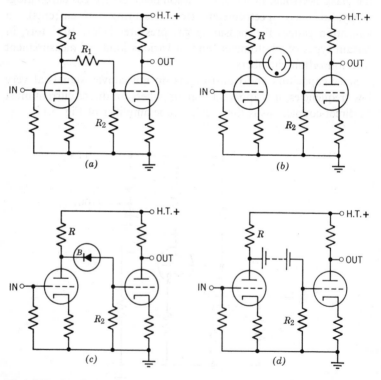

Fig. 5.12   Methods of dropping the voltage level between stages in a dc amplifier.

some loss of gain: the first because of attenuation of the signal by a factor $(R_1 + R_2)/R_2$, and the others because the current for the Zener diode or glow tube must flow through the resistors R and R_2, thus not only reducing the possible size of the anode load R but also reducing the input impedance of the following stage to R_2, so that the effective load is provided by R and R_2 in parallel.

The consequences of having unbypassed cathode resistors can be overcome by making use of the long-tailed pair circuit, in which the cathode potential remains sensibly constant in the presence of an incoming signal. The differential output which the long-tailed pair circuit provides is normally an acceptable bonus. A circuit which has been designed specifically to illustrate these points is shown in Fig. 5.13. A practical circuit would probably include some negative feedback (other than what is already present in the second stage) in order to stabilize the overall gain.

Attempts to construct dc amplifiers using transistors encounter somewhat different and more fundamental problems than those we have just described. Most of the difficulties arise because the behavior of semiconductors depends markedly on temperature, and slow temperature changes can produce drifts in the output which are sufficient to mask small changes in the voltage being measured.

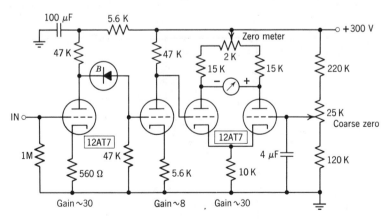

Fig. 5.13 Example of a dc amplifier (lacking overall stabilization of gain by negative feedback). Zener diode: Motorola $\frac{1}{2}$M120Z5, 120 V at 0.53 mA, dynamic impedance 1.5 K. Output meter: 0–100 μA with the 100 K series resistor.

Specifically, the leakage current i_{cbo} of a germanium transistor approximately doubles with every 8°C temperature rise, the current gain β similarly increases by an amount of the order of 1% per degree, and the base-emitter voltage v_{be} at constant emitter current decreases by about 2 mV per degree for both germanium and silicon transistors. Thus if the common-emitter amplifier of section 4c (Fig. 5.14) were to be used as a dc amplifier, the change in v_{be} alone would cause the effective input voltage to drift at the rate of 2 mV per degree.

In the case of the long-tailed pair amplifier of Fig. 5.15, the first-order effects largely cancel if the transistors are carefully matched, and the effects of leakage current can be virtually eliminated by using silicon transistors. With this type of circuit the drift is typically less than 0.1 mV per degree and can be reduced still further, if necessary, by embedding the transistors in a thermostated metal block.

Since an ac amplifier does not respond to these slow drifts, it would seem to be a good idea to convert a dc signal into alternating current by means of some sort of high-speed switch, or "chopper," amplify it, and then use a rectifier to convert back to direct current at the output, and this is in fact the method by which the best stability (typically 2 μV/°C) is obtained. A useful comparison of the per-

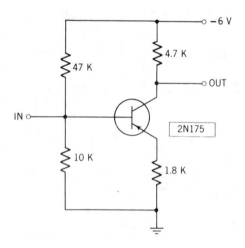

Fig. 5.14　Unsuitable circuit for a dc amplifier.

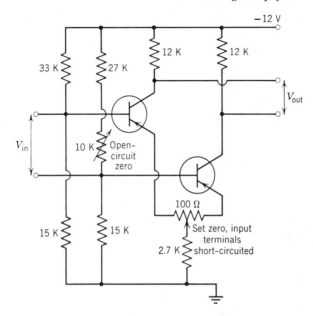

Fig. 5.15 Low-drift dc amplifier stage. Transistors: Mullard silicon type OC200, $\beta = 30$. (For complete circuits see *Mullard Reference Manual of Transistor Circuits*, Chapter 25.)

formance of different types of transistor dc amplifiers, with actual circuit diagrams, is given on page 280 of the Mullard *Reference Manual of Transistor Circuits* (see list of references at the end of this chapter).

The chopping technique is also used in many commercial vacuum tube dc amplifiers, and it appears that the best performance is obtained from electrometer-type amplifiers if the signal is chopped before being applied to the high-impedance input. This is the basis of "vibrating reed" electrometers, such as the *Cary 31* (Applied Physics Corporation) which has a detection limit of 10^{-17} ampere (about 60 electrons per second!). A block diagram of this instrument is given in Fig. 5.16. The active element is a vibrating capacitor which is driven by an oscillator at 435 cycles/sec. If the charge on the capacitor remains constant during a vibration, the capacitance and voltage must change together in accordance with the formula $q = CV$. The resulting voltage signal at 435 cycles is fed to an electrometer tube through the 33 pF capacitor C_c. The input resistor, typically 10^{11} ohms, is inserted at R_i. This type of instrument can also be used to measure very high resistances, up to 10^{15} ohms, by determining the size of the current which flows through the resistance when a known voltage is applied.

Chopper amplifiers necessarily have a limited high-frequency response because the input signal is averaged over one complete chopping cycle. The upper limit for available mechanical choppers is around one kilocycle; that for electrical (solid-state) choppers is at present a few hundred kilocycles.

Next we must consider how to obtain a very high input impedance in an electrometer. Electrometer amplifiers normally use special tubes, rather than transistors, although transistor amplifiers with quite high input impedance have been designed.[2] These transistor circuits generally make use of the high input impedance which is presented by a series of transistors in the Darlington configuration, or by emitter-follower stages when they are cascaded in the manner of Fig. 5.17. In this way the input impedance can be pushed up to about 10^9 ohms, with ordinary junction transistors, which is good enough for many purposes. With a field-effect transistor the input

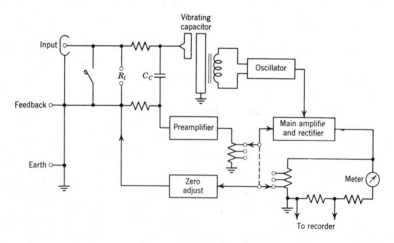

Fig. 5.16   Block diagram of Cary 31 vibrating-reed electrometer.

[2] See, for example, Bell and Venning, *Journal of Scientific Instruments*, **40**, 239 (1963).

impedance can be one or two orders of magnitude higher. An electrometer tube, on the other hand, can have an input impedance of 10^{15} ohms. Field-effect transistors naturally approach more closely to the performance level of tubes than do ordinary junction transistors, and with an *insulated-gate field-effect transistor*, such as the Texas Instruments TIXS11, or Mullard 95BFY, an input resistance of the order of 10^{12} ohms or more can be obtained. At present, however, these devices appear to be too noisy to compete with electrometer tubes.

Electrometer amplifiers are not usually required to respond to signals at more than a few hundred cycles per second: in fact, it is sometimes necessary to wait for several seconds, or even minutes, in order to obtain a steady reading with a very small current. Therefore the effect of input capacitance can be ignored, except insofar as it contributes to the time constant of the amplifier and so should be

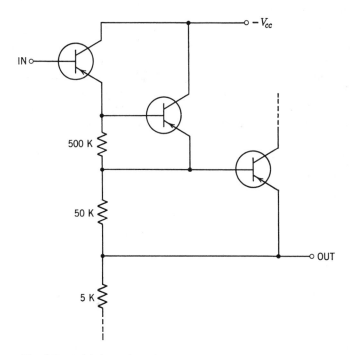

Fig. 5.17 High input impedance network of junction transistors.

reduced as much as possible. (With a resistance of 10^{12} ohms a capacitance of 1 pF, i.e., a few inches of hookup wire, has a time constant of 1 sec.) The dc conductance at the control grid of a vacuum tube is provided first by the ability of current to leak over the surface of the envelope, and second by the ability of grid current to flow inside the tube.

Surface leakage can usually be reduced to negligible proportions by choosing a tube in which the grid lead is well separated from the others at the point where it enters the envelope, by treating the envelope with insulating wax or with silicon compounds such as trimethylchlorosilane, or better, by keeping it perfectly clean and dry and enclosing the tube in a metal box which either contains a desiccant or is completely evacuated. (The box serves a double purpose, for with such high impedances very good shielding is necessary in order to avoid electromagnetic pickup.) Input leads need to be especially well insulated. Often bare wires are used, these being made stiff enough to support their own weight if they are held up in one or two places by supports of polystyrene, glass, or sapphire. Care must be taken to avoid errors caused by dielectric absorption currents, i.e., slow changes in the internal polarization of an insulator after a voltage has been applied or removed. Leakage currents may also flow over the inside of the tube envelope, and since nothing can be done about this, it may be advisable to buy several tubes and select the best one if the ultimate in performance is required.

The grid current in a vacuum tube with negative grid bias is typically about 10^{-8} ampere. This current arises from the following sources.

1. Positive ions can evaporate from the cathode and be collected by the grid.

2. Electrons which are emitted by the cathode can have sufficient thermal velocity to reach the grid.

3. Residual gas in the tube can be ionized by electrons which are on their way to the anode. Many of the ions so formed will flow to the grid.

4. If light is incident on metal parts of the tube, it can bring about the emission of photoelectrons. These electrons may either leave or strike the grid.

5.   Electrons striking the anode may have sufficient energy to bring about the emission of soft X-rays, which in turn can cause photoemission from metal surfaces.   (For many years this phenomenon set a lower limit to the pressure which could be measured with an ionization gauge.)

Electrometer tubes, such as the Mullard ME1403, GE FP54, Victoreen 5800, or Philips 4068, endeavor to remove these sources of grid current as follows:

1.   The filament is operated at a low temperature (typical filament supply 13 mA at 1.25 V) in order to reduce the thermal energy of the electrons and to reduce the likelihood that positive ions will be given off.

2.   The tube is pumped down to 10^{-7} torr, or less, during manufacture so that there is almost no residual gas to be ionized.

3.   The anode voltage is kept low (4 to 12 V) so that the electrons receive too little energy on their way to the anode either to ionize residual gas or to cause the emission of soft X-rays.

4.   The tube is kept in the dark to prevent photoemission.

With these precautions the grid current can be reduced to about 10^{-15} ampere.   Electrometer tubes may be triodes, tetrodes, or pentodes; usually the best results are obtained if there are one or

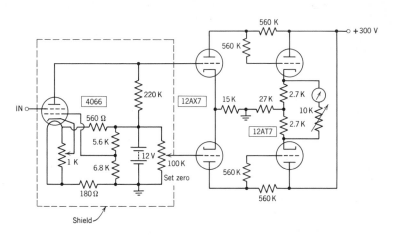

Fig. 5.18   Practical electrometer circuit.   Meter: 100, 0, $-100 \ \mu A$.

more grids between the cathode and the control grid.   Some tubes which are not specifically intended for use as electrometers can serve very well with reduced anode and filament voltage and with the input applied to a screen or suppressor grid.   Notable examples are the RCA acorn types, 954 and 959, which are now obsolete but are jealously hoarded and are still to be found giving good service in old pieces of equipment.   Barring accidents, these tubes are likely to last forever at their reduced operating voltages.

A typical electrometer amplifier is shown in Fig. 5.18.   This circuit was designed for use as a null detector in a comparison photometer (Fig. 5.19) in which the light which is incident on the two vacuum photocells is equalized by means of an external shutter.[3] This type of electrometer is also suitable for incorporation in a pH meter for use with a glass electrode when the meter has been calibrated in terms of millivolts input.   Many other electrometer circuits may be found in the literature.[4]   In critical, low-drift applications it is usually necessary to stabilize the filament supply voltage, and to use a balanced circuit configuration such as the long-tailed pair.

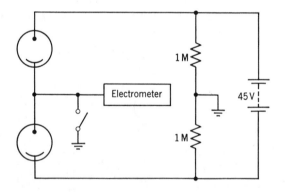

Fig. 5.19   Fluorescence photometer.   (Vacuum photo-cells type 90CV or 1P29.)

[3] W. H. Melhuish and W. S. Metcalf, *Journal of the Chemical Society* (*London*), **157**, 976 (1954).

[4] See D. C. Frost, in *Mass spectrometry*, edited by C. A. McDowell, Chapter 6.   New York: McGraw-Hill Book Company, 1963.

EXERCISES

5.1 Design a long-tailed pair stage using a 12AX7 double triode ($\mu = 100$, and $\rho = 80$ K), choosing the operating point of each section at $i_a = 0.5$ mA and $v_a = 100$ V. The supply voltage is 300 V, and the voltage gain, in terms of $v_1 - v_2$, is required to be at least 60.

5.2 (a) Taking the anode characteristics of a 12AT7 tube section (Fig. 4.19), draw the load line with intercepts $i_a = 10$ mA at $v_a = 0$ and $v_a = 270$ V at $i_a = 0$. What are the values of the supply voltage and load resistance? From this line read off corresponding values of i_a and v_g at its intersections with the individual characteristics. We suppose that the circuit is a cathode follower, and that the load is provided by a cathode resistor R_k. Plot a graph of v_g against i_a and, on the same axes, plot $-i_a R_k$ against i_a. Hence read off values of $v_{in} = v_g + i_a R_k$ and $v_{out} = i_a R_k$. Plot v_{in} against v_{out} and comment on the result.

(b) The output characteristics for a transistor in the common-base configuration are given below. Draw the load line which corresponds to V_{cc} (supply voltage) $= -12$ V with a collector load of 1.2 K. Comment on the significance of this line. If the input impedance is 25 ohms, what is the voltage gain?

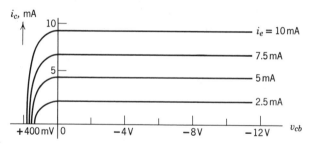

Ex. 5.2

5.3 Show that for a triode amplifier stage with anode load R_a and an unbypassed cathode resistor R_k the voltage gain at the anode is given by

$$-\frac{dv_{out}}{dv_{in}} = \frac{\mu R_a}{\rho + R_a + (1 + \mu)R_k}$$

where $dv_g = dv_{in} - R_k \, di_a$, $dv_{out} = -R_a \, di_a$, $dv_a = -(R_a + R_k) \, di_a$, and the symbols have their usual meanings. Comment on the behavior of the circuit when R_k is of similar magnitude to $R_a + \rho$. What is the voltage gain at the cathode?

5.4 Derive expressions to describe the behavior of a transistor long-tailed pair amplifier with a shared emitter resistor R_e and equal load resistors R, and with an impedance Z in series with the base input resistance of each transistor (cf. Fig. 5.3).   Results are

$$0 = dv_2\left(\frac{Z + r_{be}}{\beta R} + \frac{R_e}{R}\right) + dv_1\frac{R_e}{R}$$

and

$$\frac{dv_1 - dv_2}{dv_{in}} = -\frac{\beta R}{Z + R_{be}}$$

REFERENCES

1. *Mullard reference manual of transistor circuits.*   London: Mullard, Ltd., 1960, Chapter 25.

2. E. Wolfendale, *The transistor.*   London: Heywood and Company, 1963, Chapter 9.

3. H. A. Romanowitz, *Fundamentals of semiconductor and tube electronics.* New York: John Wiley & Sons, Inc., 1962, Chapters 11 and 12.

4. R. J. Watts, "DC amplifiers," in W. C. Elmore and M. Sands, *Electronics.* New York: McGraw-Hill, 1949, p. 180.

5. H. V. Malmstadt, C. G. Enke, and E. C. Toren, Jr., *Electronics for scientists.*   New York: W. A. Benjamin, 1963, Chapters 3 and 4.

6

Rectifiers and Detectors

6a INTRODUCTION

The function of a rectifier or detector is simply to convert alternating current into direct current.   For a rectifier the objective is usually to convert ac power from the mains into dc power which can be smoothed and regulated and used to drive other electronic equipment. For a detector the aim is to extract the information which is contained in the variable amplitude of an ac signal by converting the signal to direct current.   The process involved is actually the same in both cases.

The rectification process is illustrated in Fig. 6.1.   If the sine wave of Fig. 6.1*a*, whose average current in the forward direction is zero, is passed into a circuit which has a low resistance in the forward direction and a very high resistance in the reverse direction, i.e., a circuit containing a diode, the negative-going peaks are eliminated and the average current in the forward direction is greater than zero (Fig. 6.1*b*).   This is termed *half-wave rectification*.   If the negative-going peaks can be inverted and added to the positive peaks, as in Fig. 6.1*c*, a higher average current is obtained, and this is termed *full-wave rectification*.   Half-wave rectification is adequate for the detection of small signals and for power supplies which are only required to deliver small currents (less than about 10 mA), for example, the high-voltage supplies for photomultipliers or cathode-ray tubes.   When moderate or high currents are to be delivered, full-wave rectification is preferred.

Some typical waveforms that are encountered when dealing with detectors for small signals are shown in Fig. 6.2.   If the sine wave of Fig. 6.1*a* has its amplitude controlled by the magnitude of an input signal, as in Fig. 6.2*a*, it is said to function as a carrier wave and to be *amplitude-modulated* (am).   The information derived from the signal is contained in the modulation, so that if the modulation exceeds 100%, as in Fig. 6.2*b*, some information is lost.   When the signal of Fig. 6.2*a* is rectified, the information which was contained in the modulation now appears in the average dc current, as shown in Fig. 6.2*c*.   A signal can also be *frequency-modulated* (fm), as in Fig. 6.2*d*.   This is achieved by causing the input signal to vary one element, usually a capacitance, in a tuned circuit which is part of the oscillator that generates the carrier wave.   Once the fm signal has been amplified to the desired level, it is converted to an am signal before being rectified.   This is done by passing the signal into a resonant circuit (cf. section 1c) which is such that the whole range of frequencies in the fm signal falls on one side of the resonance peak in a region where the response is almost a linear function of frequency (Fig. 6.3).   Frequency modulation has advantages over amplitude modulation for high-fidelity radio transmission but is not very common in laboratory equipment.

An alternative method of obtaining a modulated ac signal is to take a dc signal, such as that of Fig. 6.4*a*, and interrupt it periodically with a chopper (cf. section 5d).   The result of doing this is shown

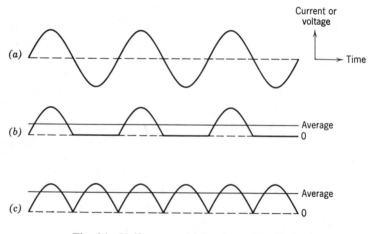

Fig. 6.1   Half-wave and full-wave rectification.

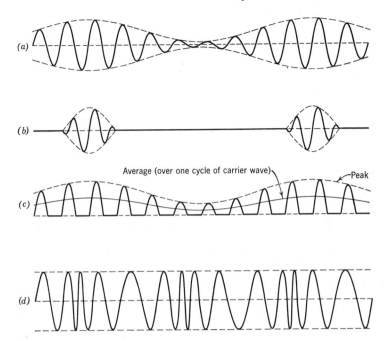

Fig. 6.2 Detector waveforms.

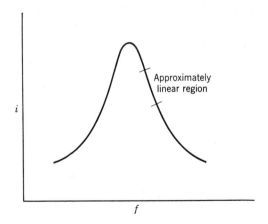

Fig. 6.3 Conversion of frequency modulation to amplitude modulation.

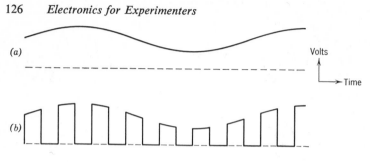

Fig. 6.4   Chopping a dc signal: (*a*) before, (*b*) after.

in Fig. 6.4*b*.   If the chopped signal is then passed through a resonant circuit or tuned amplifier (these are described in Chapter 7), only the ac component of the signal at the chopping frequency is selected, and the appearance of the signal is similar to Fig. 6.2*a*.

After the original signal has been converted into modulated alternating current, it can be amplified by means of a stable ac amplifier and then detected, or "demodulated," i.e., converted back to its original form.   The type of rectifier used at this stage depends mainly on the amount of signal that was available to begin with. The most interesting situation, and the one most often encountered in laboratory work, occurs when the original signal is extremely small; we shall discuss this case at some length in section 6c.   The discussion of noise, gain, and bandwidth in Chapter 8 is also relevant here.   In section 6b we consider rectifiers and smoothing networks from the point of view of dc power supplies.   In section 6d we briefly consider some applications of diodes in pulse circuits.

6b   RECTIFIERS AND SMOOTHING NETWORKS

A typical circuit which contains a half-wave rectifier and an *RC* smoothing network is given in Fig. 6.5.   The rectifier tube is one that is designed for an input of 7800 V rms[1] at 2 mA.   Its filament draws 300 mA at 1.5 V.   The tube could be replaced by a semiconductor diode or metal rectifier of equivalent rating.   (The term "metal rectifier" is applied to semiconductor rectifiers based on selenium or

[1] The root-mean-square (rms) voltage is $1/\sqrt{2}$ times the peak voltage for a sinusoidal waveform.   The peak-to-peak voltage is twice the peak voltage.

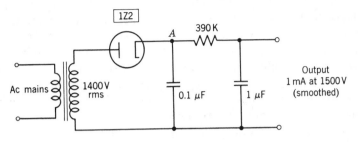

Fig. 6.5   Half-wave rectifier with *RC* smoothing network.

cuprous oxide.)   In the absence of the smoothing capacitors the voltage or current waveform at the cathode of the rectifier would be as in Fig. 6.6a.

In the presence of the 0.1 μF smoothing capacitor the impedance at the cathode is only about 2.7 K at 50 or 60 cycles, and so a large initial current flows (shaded area in Fig. 6.6b).   This current would rapidly destroy the rectifier if it were maintained, but once the capacitor has charged to the peak voltage the charge can only leak away slowly through the 390 K resistor and so the diode is reverse-biased for the remainder of the cycle.   When the current has ceased to flow from the rectifier, the capacitor discharges with a time constant $RC = 390$ K $\times$ 0.1 μF = 0.04 sec.   The voltage at *A* is therefore represented by the solid line in Fig. 6.6b.   During the next cycle current does not begin to flow through the diode until it is forward-biased once more, so that much less current flows than during the first charging cycle.   The resulting rectifier current waveforms are

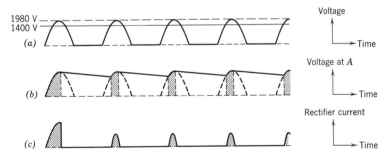

Fig. 6.6   Waveforms in circuit of Fig. 6.5.

shown in Fig. 6.6c.   The peaks and valleys (*ripple*) on the solid waveform of Fig. 6.6b receive additional smoothing from the combination of the 1 μF capacitor and 1.2 M load (time constant 1.2 sec), which together comprise a second filter section.   It would not be advisable to use a much larger capacitor in the first filter section because the current flow during the charging cycle—the "hot switching transient"—would be excessive.   The maximum value of the input capacitor, or alternatively, the maximum values of peak plate current and average plate current, are normally included in the data supplied by the manufacturers of rectifier diodes.

Two possible ways of achieving full-wave rectification are shown in Fig. 6.7.   The first circuit, a bridge rectifier, is often used to provide direct current for battery chargers and other low-voltage equipment. The second uses a transformer with a center-tapped secondary in

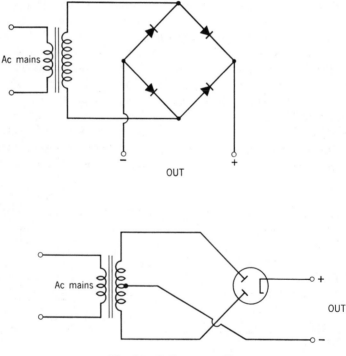

Fig. 6.7   Full-wave rectifiers.

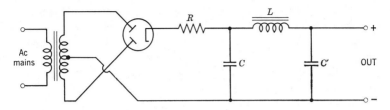

Fig. 6.8   Full-wave rectifier with *LC* smoothing.

combination with a double diode (or two separate diodes).   In this case the output voltage is half the total secondary voltage of the transformer.   This is the arrangement that is most commonly found in dc power supplies.   When large currents are to be smoothed, the *RC* network of Fig. 6.5 is wasteful of voltage, and it is preferable to use *LC* smoothing, as in Fig. 6.8.   In a typical circuit the transformer would supply 350, 0, and −350 V rms, the capacitors *C* and *C′* would be from 4 to 50 μF, and the iron-cored inductance, or "choke," *L*, would be 10 H.   The purpose of the resistor *R* is to limit the current which is drawn from the rectifier during the charging cycle of the capacitor *C*. The minimum value of this limiting resistor for a given value of input capacitance is usually specified by the makers of the rectifier.   A typical value would be 220 ohms.   With a suitable rectifier, for example, a GZ33, 5V4, EZ81, or two 1N547, this circuit would be expected to deliver up to several hundred milliamperes, with an open-circuit voltage of about 470 V direct current appearing at the output terminals of the smoothing network.   The output is well in excess of 350 V because the input capacitor *C* tends to charge up to the peak voltage at the cathode of the rectifier (Fig. 6.9).   This high output

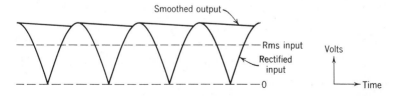

Fig. 6.9   Action of a peak rectifier.

is an advantage because 100 V or more is usually lost in the subsequent process of producing a regulated output voltage (see Chapter 7).

If the capacitor C and resistor R are removed, so that current flows directly into the inductance L ("choke input" instead of "capacitor input"), the current which is drawn from the rectifier is more evenly distributed over a cycle and a higher average current can safely be obtained from a given rectifier. On the other hand, the "peak rectifier" action of the input capacitor is lacking and the open-circuit output voltage is only slightly above the rms input voltage.

6c DETECTORS FOR SMALL SIGNALS

Diode Detectors. Half-wave rectification is all that is required with small signals, and essentially the same factors apply as in the previous discussion of half-wave rectifiers for power supplies. The signal frequency is generally much higher than the 50 or 60 cycles of the ac mains, and the smoothing capacitors can be correspondingly smaller. Figure 6.10 shows a circuit in which a simple diode detector with an 0.047 μF smoothing capacitor forms part of a bridge-balance indicator for conductivity measurements.[2] The circuit is designed to respond to the out-of-balance signal, whose frequency is a few kilocycles, and the meter is connected so that its reading decreases in the presence of an incoming signal. In practice the meter is first set at near full-scale deflection with no input signal; then, with the signal generator turned on, the bridge resistance and capacitance arms are adjusted to give a maximum meter reading.

In radio receivers it is fairly common practice to use the cathode and control grid of a tube as a diode for rectification of an incoming signal which is large enough to drive the tube into the grid current region. The amplified signal is then distorted in a manner which approximates half-wave rectification (Fig. 6.11a). This arrangement is known as a grid-leak, or "leaky grid," detector. A tube that is driven into the grid current region is also used occasionally to square the top of a sine wave or pulse when a square-wave output is desired (Fig. 6.11b). The bottom of the sine wave can be squared

[2] See, for example, Daniels et al., *Experimental physical chemistry.* New York: McGraw-Hill Book Company, Fourth Edition, 1949, p. 454, or the corresponding section (on electrolytic conductance) in later editions.

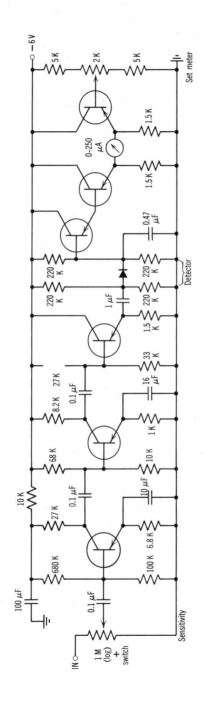

Fig. 6.10 Bridge balance indicator. Detector: Any general-purpose diode, e.g., Mullard OA81. Transistors: $\beta \geqslant 50$, V_{ce} (max) $\geqslant 10\,\text{V}$, i_{ce} (max) $\geqslant 5\,\text{mA}$, e.g., Mullard OC75 ($\beta = 90$).

131

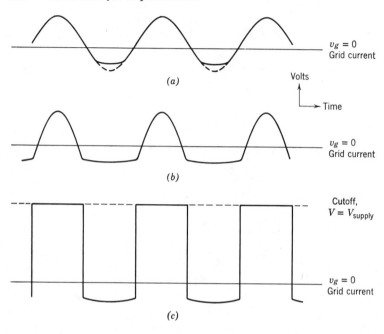

Fig. 6.11   Rectification (*a*) and (*b*), and squaring (*c*) by the grid and cathode of a tube acting as a diode.   Voltages measured at the anode load, so that in (*c*) it is the top which is squared by cutoff.

by the same tube if the input signal is sufficiently large to drive it into cutoff at the other extreme of the grid voltage excursion (Fig. 6.11*c*).

Phase-Sensitive Detectors.   In the last chapter we noted that the most effective way of amplifying a small dc signal is to begin by converting it to alternating current with the aid of a mechanical or electrical chopper.   Once the resulting ac signal has been amplified, we then have the problem of how best to convert back to direct current.   Obviously a simple diode would do the trick, but if, as is often the case, we are interested in pushing the apparatus to its limits in order to measure a very small signal, the diode detector has the disadvantage that it rectifies signals indiscriminately, whether or not they were present in the output from the chopper.   The result is that extraneous signals, in the form of amplifier noise, pickup, and microphonics (see Chapter 8), are all present in the rectified output.

A phase-sensitive detector, of which there are many varieties and almost as many names (e.g., gated detector, coherent detector, synchronous detector), solves this problem by rectifying only signals that are of the same frequency as the chopper and *of the same phase as the chopped signal.* Provided the dc voltage changes which are being measured are fairly slow, it is then possible to remove much of the random noise which was present in the original unchopped signal by averaging the output over a period of time. (This can be done by passing the signal through a filter network of the appropriate time constant—for example, one or two seconds.)

A phase-sensitive detector works by taking a *reference signal* from the chopper and converting it into a square wave (see Chapter 9 for methods of doing this) which is used to turn a tube or transistor on and off in time with the chopper. If the amplified ac signal, which is necessarily in phase with the reference signal, is passed through this tube or transistor, it will be turned off by the "gate" signal for exactly half of each cycle and the output will be equivalent to that from a half-wave rectifier (Fig. 6.12*a*). A signal that is of the same

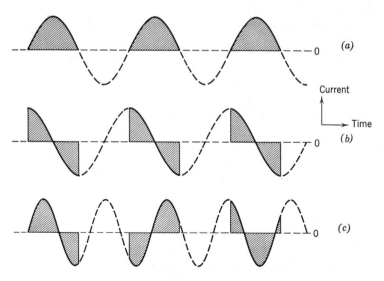

Fig. 6.12 Phase-sensitive detection: (*a*) signal and gate of same frequency and phase, (*b*) signal and gate 90° out of phase, (*c*) signal of different frequency from gate. Shaded areas indicate current passed by the gate.

frequency as the chopper but not of the same phase will give some contribution to the output, the amount of the contribution depending on the relative phase of this signal and of the gate (Fig. 6.12*b*). Noise signals will be of random phase, so that on the average their contribution will cancel out, even if they are of the correct frequency. A signal of the wrong frequency will sometimes give a positive output and sometimes a negative one so that the time average of the output is also zero in this case (Fig. 6.12*c*).

One form of phase-sensitive detector is shown in Fig. 6.13. The 6GY6 tube which is used here has been specifically designed for operation as a "gated amplifier." The suppressor grid g_3 is much more closely wound than is usually the case and in fact is to be regarded as a second control grid. If this grid is at a potential of -10 V with respect to the cathode, the tube is completely cut off, but if it is at the cathode potential, the tube behaves as a pentode of plate resistance $\rho = 140$ K and transconductance $g_m = 3.7 \times 10^{-3}$ ohm^{-1}. This type of circuit has many applications; the smoothing capaictor in parallel with the anode load is included if it is to be used as a detector. Other tubes with more than one control grid, for example, hexodes and heptodes, can also be used in this way.

The simplest form of transistorized phase-sensitive detector is shown in Fig. 6.14*a*. When the square-wave signal is positive the transistor is cut off, so that it behaves as a high resistance and the

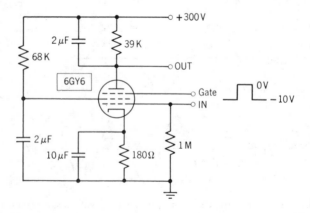

Fig. 6.13   A gated amplifier or detector.

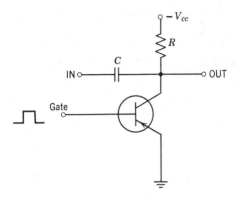

Fig. 6.14*a* Transistor used as a phase-sensitive detector.

input voltage signal appears across *R*. When the square-wave signal is negative the transistor is turned full on ("bottomed"), so that the collector-base diode is forward-biased and the input signal flows to earth through the transistor. The capacitor *C* must be large enough so that the time constant *RC* is too great for the capacitor to charge through *R* while the transistor is cut off. It is obvious that this same circuit, less the capacitor *C*, could be used to chop or "gate" the signal initially.

If the simple circuit of Fig. 6.14*a* is used to gate a very small signal, a source of error appears which is highly important for chopper circuits in general. When the transistor is turned full on,

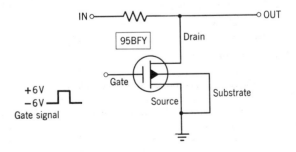

Fig. 6.14*b* Gating circuit with extremely low offset voltage.

the conduction path is equivalent to two forward-biased diodes, and in the absence of any input signal the circuit will have an output which is equal to the difference between the forward voltages of the diodes. This *offset voltage* is temperature-dependent and therefore drift-prone, and sets a lower limit to the size of the signal with which the chopper can be employed. The conduction path in a field-effect transistor, however, is purely resistive, so in this case the offset voltage is zero and there only remains an offset *current*. This, the leakage current through the gate to the conduction channel, is entirely negligible in an insulated-gate FET. A typical FET chopper circuit,[3] using a Mullard 95BFY *n*-channel insulated-gate FET, is illustrated in Fig. 6.14*b*.

A more elaborate circuit, using vacuum tubes, is shown in Fig. 6.15. In this circuit the amplified input signal is split into two out-of-phase signals by means of a long-tailed pair (section 5b), and the two halves of the signal are applied to the grids of the lower 12AT7 double triode. The upper double triode is turned off for half of each cycle by the square-wave reference signal, so that if the reference signal and input signal are in phase a net dc voltage appears across the output. When the upper tubes are cut off the lower tubes still conduct by way of the 6AL5 double diode. This means that the cathode potentials of the upper tubes cannot fall below +110 V (neglecting the small forward voltages across the diode sections), and so there is no doubt that the reference signal will cause these tubes to cut off. During the ON part of the cycle the cathode potentials of the upper tubes are close to 150 V because of cathode-follower action, and the diodes are reverse-biased. The linearity of the response of this circuit is very good, largely because of negative feedback which results from the presence of the unbypassed 27 K cathode resistors (cf. section 7b).

An alternative and rather elegant procedure for dealing with very small signals in the presence of noise[4] is to chop them, add some of

---

[3] For a discussion of the operation of this circuit and the limitations which are encountered at high switching rates, see p. 23 of the publication *Mullard 95BFY development type metal-oxide-semiconductor transistor*. London: Mullard, Ltd., 1964.

[4] R. H. Dicke, *Review of Scientific Instruments*, **17**, 268 (1947). For a commercial example of this form of "lock-in" amplifier see *Bulletin 109*, Princeton Applied Research Corporation (Box 565, Princeton, N.J.).

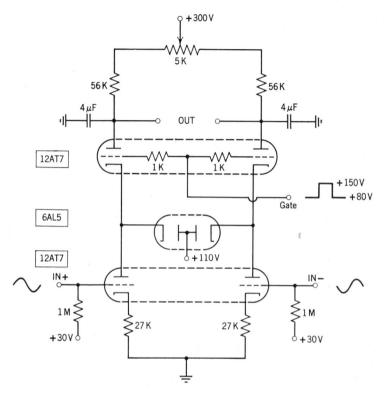

Fig. 6.15 Balanced phase-sensitive detector.

the chopping signal in the form of a square wave, and amplify the combined signal with a tuned amplifier. The contribution from the chopping signal is finally subtracted as a zero correction. With this system the main benefit is gained from the possibility of using a very sharply tuned amplifier to increase the size of the signal relative to the noise. In the absence of the added signal from the chopper the phase of the total signal is largely decided by the random phase of the noise of the frequency which is passed by the amplifier, and the contribution from the signal averages out to zero. The use of narrow-band amplification also prevents the amplifier from being overloaded by the noise. A simple transistor circuit for mixing the

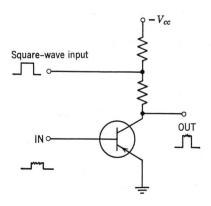

Fig. 6.16   Simple circuit for adding two signals together.

input signal with that from the chopper is shown in Fig. 6.16.   The
problem of separating signals from noise is discussed more fully in
Chapter 8.

6d   DIODE PULSE CIRCUITS

Small signals in the form of discrete pulses are encountered in
many research instruments, notably those involved in the measurement of nuclear radiation.   A series diode (Fig. 6.17a) acts as a
pulse-height discriminator because the diode is at first reverse-biased

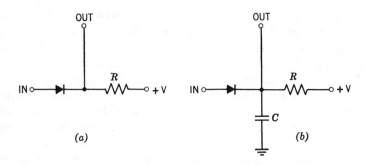

Fig. 6.17   Series diode networks.

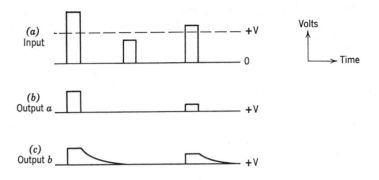

Fig. 6.18 Series diode waveforms.

and the pulse is not transmitted until its voltage rises above $+V$ (Figs. 6.18a and 6.18b). If a capacitor is added as in Fig. 6.17b, the output pulse decays with time constant RC (Fig. 6.18c) and the circuit also acts as a pulse lengthener. If a "train" of pulses is applied to the RC network of Fig. 6.19a, the output is evenly distributed with respect to earth potential, as in Fig. 6.20a (assuming the time constant RC to be much greater than the interval between pulses; cf. section 1c).

If a diode is connected in parallel with R, as in Fig. 6.19b, it conducts when the signal is positive but not when it is negative. The diode then acts as a peak rectifier and the capacitor C charges to a negative voltage which is close to the maximum voltage amplitude of the pulse train. (This requires that RC is much greater than the interval between pulses.) The result is that the top of the pulse train is fixed at earth potential, as in Fig. 6.20b, and the diode is said

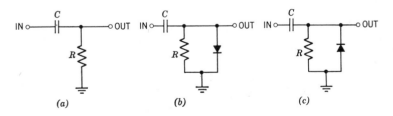

Fig. 6.19 Clamping networks.

to act as a *dc clamp* or *dc restorer*. If the diode is reversed, as in Fig. 6.19c, the bottom of the pulse train is clamped, as in Fig. 6.20c. If the diode is connected to a point whose potential is different from zero, the top or bottom of the pulse train is clamped at this potential.

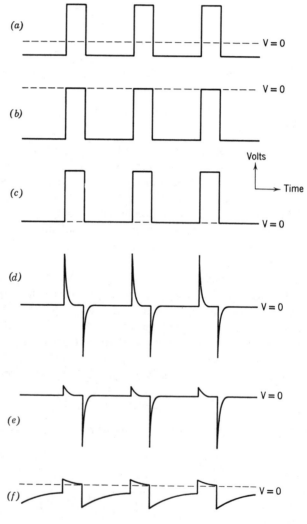

Fig. 6.20 Waveforms in parallel diode circuits.

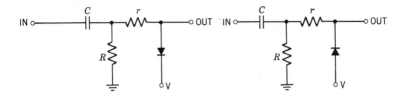

Fig. 6.21   Clipping networks.

If the time constant RC is much less than the interval between pulses, the circuit of Fig. 6.19a behaves as a differentiating network and the output is as shown in Fig. 6.20d.   The diode then attenuates one of the voltage spikes relative to the other in the ratio of its forward resistance to R, as in Fig. 6.20e.   With intermediate time constants intermediate behavior is observed, as in Fig. 6.20f.

If the diode is in series with a resistance r (which may be the internal resistance of the pulse generator) which is such that rC is much greater than the interval between pulses, the potential of the output is prevented from rising above the potential V if the diode is connected as in Fig. 6.21a, or from falling below V if the diode is connected as in Fig. 6.21b.   The result is that the tops or bottoms of the output pulses are squared, or "clipped."   (This is the basis of the grid-leak detector which was described in the last section.)

The operations we have described—differentiation, integration, dc restoration, height discrimination, and clipping—together comprise a fairly complete armory for dealing with signals that consist of a series of regularly or irregularly spaced pulses.   Some other circuits for handling or generating pulse signals are described in Chapter 9.

EXERCISES

6.1   Look up the characteristics of several rectifiers in tube and semiconductor manuals.   Note values of peak inverse voltage, limiting resistance, maximum input capacitance, and rectified current, and choose appropriate values for the components in smoothing networks similar to those in Figs. 6.5 and 6.8.

6.2 Compare the ratio of V_{out} to V_{in} in terms of measured voltages for the following choke input filter, both for direct current and for alternating current of the mains frequency and of twice the mains frequency (note that with full-wave rectification the major component of the ripple is of twice the mains frequency).

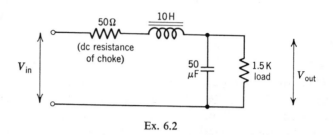

Ex. 6.2

6.3 Show that for the circuit shown below the output voltage is approximately twice the peak ac input voltage, i.e., the circuit functions as a *voltage doubler*. Design a similar circuit using a double diode tube.

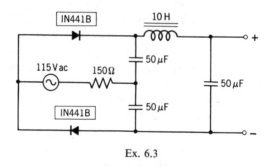

Ex. 6.3

6.4 Draw a block diagram, showing all the necessary elements, for a complete chopper-stabilized dc amplifier for very small signals.

6.5 Verify that the function of a smoothing network is essentially one of integration. If a signal $e_0 \sin(\omega t + \delta)$ is turned on and off periodically at times $0, t_1, 2t_1, \ldots$, show by integrating the signal from 0 to t_1 that the smoothed output voltage is a maximum for $t_1 = \pi/\omega$ and $\delta = 0$. Relate this result to the operation of a phase-sensitive detector.

6.6 How would you convert a positive-going square wave (base line at earth potential) into (a) two short pulses, one positive and one negative; (b) two short negative pulses (cf. full-wave rectification), with the base line at -10 V; (c) a single positive pulse; (d) a truncated positive pulse; (e) a voltage step, $V = 0$, $t < t_1$: $V = V$, $t > t_1$. (This corresponds to a very long pulse.)

REFERENCES

1. Philip Parker, *Electronics*. London: Edward Arnold, 1950, Chapter 14.
2. H. A. Romanowitz, *Fundamentals of semiconductor and tube electronics*. New York: John Wiley & Sons, Inc., 1962, Chapters 4 and 6.
3. E. J. Bair, *Introduction to chemical instrumentation*. New York: McGraw-Hill Book Company, 1962, sections 5.6, 7.4, 7.5.
4. F. J. M. Farley. *Elements of pulse circuits*. London: Methuen & Co., 1955, Chapter 2.

7

Feedback

....

7a INTRODUCTION

Feedback occurs when some of the output from a system is returned to the input. If the output is fed back in such a way that it subtracts from the input, this is termed "negative feedback," while if it adds to the input, this is termed "positive feedback." The occurrence of feedback is not confined to electronics—negative feedback in particular is an essential part of all self-regulatory systems, for example, thermostat baths, servomechanisms, bodies in stable planetary orbits, and animal populations in the presence of limited food supplies. The study of the applications of negative feedback in general has been given the name *cybernetics*. Less attention has been paid to the role of positive feedback,[1] which occurs in nature in auto-catalyzed reactions, in the growth of business capital, and in the growth of animal populations in the presence of unlimited food supplies. Negative feedback is invariably a stabilizing factor, since it tends to cut down the effect of any change in the input, and typical applications in electronics are to stable-gain amplifiers, narrow-bandwidth amplifiers, and regulated power supplies. These are the applications which will be described here. Positive feedback tends to magnify the effect of small fluctuations at the input and has important applications in oscillators and switching circuits. Some of these applications are described in Chapter 9.

Consider the circuit of Fig. 7.1, in which a fraction ϕ of the output

[1] M. Maruyama, *American Scientist*, **51**, 164 (1963).

signal from an amplifier is fed back to the input.[2] The unfedback amplifier has gain A (the *open-loop gain*). The fedback amplifier has gain A', which is given by

$$A(dV_{in} + \phi\, dV_{out}) = dV_{out} \qquad (7.1)$$

or

$$A' = \frac{dV_{out}}{dV_{in}} = \frac{A}{1 - \phi A} \qquad (7.2)$$

The ratio of A to A' is termed the *loop gain*. If ϕA is large equation (7.2) reduces to

$$A' = -\frac{1}{\phi} \qquad (7.3)$$

If ϕA is small and positive the gain A' is higher than A and increases as ϕA tends to unity. With ϕA equal to unity the gain becomes infinite and the smallest input signal will cause the output signal to increase to the point at which the amplifier overloads. In this case the circuit constitutes a self-sustaining oscillator and is obviously not much use as an amplifier. By means of a suitable frequency-dependent feedback network it is possible to arrange that oscillation occurs only within a very narrow frequency range, so that the output has the form of a pure sine wave. Such a circuit can be a very useful signal generator.

If ϕA is negative the gain A' with feedback is always less than A, and if $|\phi A|$ is sufficiently large the gain is governed mainly by the characteristics of the feedback loop and is virtually independent of the characteristics of the amplifier [equation (7.3)]. Since the feedback loop is normally composed of passive circuit elements, with

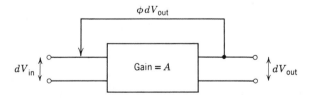

Fig. 7.1 Amplifier with feedback.

[2] This fraction is commonly labeled β. We prefer to use the symbol ϕ to avoid confusion with the β of a transistor.

their stable characteristics and linear response, this means that the amplifier is similarly stable and linear. To illustrate these remarks, suppose that $A = 1000$ and 1% of the output is taken back to the input as negative feedback, i.e., ϕ is -0.01. From equation (7.2) we find A' to be 90.9. Now if A suddenly changes to 1100, the new value of A' is 91.7, and we see that a 10% change in A produces only a 0.8% change in A'. If the gain A varies with the size of the input signal, i.e., the amplifier is not linear, these variations will similarly be reduced by feedback and linearity will be greatly improved.

Apart from the gain, the most important characteristics of an amplifier are its input and output impedances. These impedances are also affected by feedback, the effect of negative voltage feedback being to increase the input impedance and decrease the output impedance.[3] We consider this in general terms as follows (Fig. 7.2). Let Z_i and Z_o be the input and output impedances of the amplifier without feedback. In the presence of feedback the voltage across Z_i is $dV_{in} + \phi\, dV_{out}$, so we have

$$dV_{in} + \phi\, dV_{out} = di_{in}Z_i \tag{7.4}$$

and making use of (7.2) we find

$$\frac{dV_{in}}{1 - \phi A} = di_{in}Z_i \tag{7.5}$$

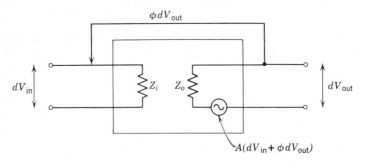

Fig. 7.2   Effect of feedback on input and output impedances.

[3] Negative *current* feedback causes the input impedance to decrease and the output impedance to increase. (Cf. Exercise 7.3.) See, for example, L. B. Arguimbau, *Vacuum-tube circuits and transistors*. New York: John Wiley & Sons, Inc., 1957, p. 397.

Hence the input impedance in presence of feedback is given by

$$Z_1' = \frac{\partial V_{\text{in}}}{\partial i_{\text{in}}} = (1 - \phi A)Z_i \qquad (7.6)$$

For the case $A = 1000$ and $\phi = -0.01$ the negative feedback raises the input impedance by a factor of 11.

To calculate the output impedance we imagine a voltage dV_{out} to be applied to the output terminals, with $dV_{\text{in}} = 0$. Feedback now gives rise to a voltage $\phi A \, dV_{\text{out}}$ at the output terminals. The voltage which actually appears across Z_o is therefore equal to

$$dV_{\text{out}}(1 - \phi A) = di_{\text{out}}Z_o \qquad (7.7)$$

Hence the output impedance in the presence of feedback is given by

$$Z_0' = \frac{\partial V_{\text{out}}}{\partial i_{\text{out}}} = \frac{Z_o}{1 - \phi A} \qquad (7.8)$$

The output impedance is seen to be reduced by negative feedback by the same factor as the amplifier gain, and this is also the factor by which the input impedance is increased, namely, the loop gain $1 - \phi A$. This quantity also describes the stabilization of the gain which is produced by the negative feedback, for if we differentiate equation (7.2) we find

$$\frac{(1 - \phi A) \, dA'}{A'} = \frac{dA}{A} \qquad (7.9)$$

so that if the open-loop gain A changes by $x\%$ the gain with feedback changes by only $x/(1 - \phi A)\%$.

In the next section we consider some practical circuits for applying negative feedback to amplifiers.

7b SINGLE-STAGE AMPLIFIERS WITH FEEDBACK

A cathode follower or emitter follower is an example of an amplifier with practically 100% voltage feedback, for if the grid or base voltage alters, the current through the cathode or emitter load alters in such a way as to practically cancel the effect of the voltage change. The role of the negative feedback is more easily seen for

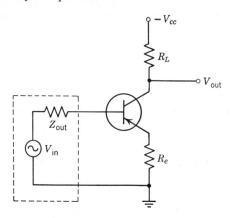

Fig. 7.3   Feedback via an unbypassed emitter resistor.

the related case of a common-cathode or common-emitter stage with an unbypassed cathode or emitter resistor (cf. Exercise 5.3).   For the transistor (Fig. 7.3) we have, neglecting the effect of changes in the emitter potential,

$$A = \frac{dV_{\text{out}}}{dV_{\text{in}}} = -\frac{\beta R_L}{R_e + r_{be} + Z_{\text{out}}} \qquad (7.10)$$

Negative feedback occurs because the voltage change across the emitter resistor tends to subtract from any change in base potential. The fraction of the output signal which is fed back to the input is $R_e/R_L = \phi$, so that the gain with feedback included is

$$A' = -\frac{\beta R_L}{r_{be} + Z_{\text{out}} + (\beta + 1)R_e} \sim -\frac{R_L}{R_e} \qquad (7.11)$$

Provided β, R_L, and R_e are large the gain of the stage is virtually independent of variations in β, r_{be}, or Z_{out}.

For the corresponding common-cathode stage (Fig. 7.4) the open-loop gain is seen to be

$$A = -\frac{\mu R_L}{R_L + R_k + \rho} \qquad (7.12)$$

The fraction of the output which is fed back to the input is R_k/R_L,

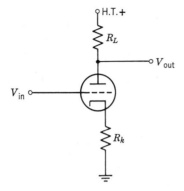

Fig. 7.4 Feedback via an unbypassed cathode resistor.

so the gain with feedback is given by

$$A' = -\frac{\mu R_L}{R_L + \rho + (\mu + 1)R_k} \sim -\frac{R_L}{R_k} \qquad (7.13)$$

This is the same as the result which was obtained directly in Exercise
5.3. It is important to note that in these two circuits we are applying
current, or *series*, feedback, and the result is to decrease the input
impedance and increase the output impedance (cf. Exercise 7.1).

An alternative method of applying negative feedback to a single
stage is shown in Figs. 7.5 and 7.6. Since the input and output
signals are of opposite phase, the negative voltage feedback can be
achieved simply by making a direct connection between them. For
the circuit of Fig. 7.5 we have $\phi = R_g/(R_f + R_g)$, and for the circuit
of Fig. 7.6 we have $\phi = r_{be}/(R_f + r_{be})$, where the biasing resistors
R_1 and R_2 are assumed to be much greater than the base input
resistance r_{be}. This method is not ideal for the transistor because
the nonlinearity of r_{be} is reflected in nonlinearity of the gain, even
when feedback is present. The linearity could be improved by
inserting a resistance r in series with r_{be}, but this would reduce the
open-loop gain. In both of these circuits the capacitor C must be
large enough so that it introduces negligible phase shift into the
feedback loop at low frequencies; otherwise the feedback may turn
out to be positive when the phase shift within the tube or transistor

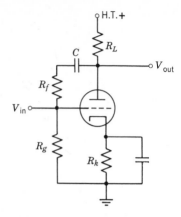

Fig. 7.5   Feedback from anode to grid.

is taken into account.   Similar feedback by way of the grid to plate capacitance (Miller effect) is responsible for the misbehavior of triode amplifier stages at high frequencies.   At frequencies for which this feedback is negative the result is an undesirable loss of gain; at frequencies for which the feedback is positive the result is instability and a tendency to oscillate.   This subject is taken up again in Chapter 8.

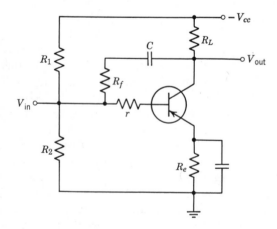

Fig. 7.6   Feedback from collector to base.

7c FEEDBACK IN MULTISTAGE AMPLIFIERS

In order to obtain the best results from an amplifier employing negative feedback, it is necessary for the open-loop gain to be as large as possible, so that $A\phi$ and $1/\phi$ can both be large. This suggests that it would be a good idea to apply a relatively small amount of feedback over several stages of amplification. The only objection is that phase shifts occurring within a tube or transistor at high frequencies, and in interstage coupling elements at low frequencies, can cause trouble if the feedback loop extends over more than two or three stages. Large multistage amplifiers with feedback stabilization are therefore likely to contain two or more feedback loops working independently of one another.

An example of a transistor amplifier with feedback applied over several stages is shown in Fig. 7.7. With the switch closed the effect of the feedback loop is such that the output signal tends to drive the emitter of the first transistor in the same direction that the input signal drives the base, so the feedback is indeed negative.

Let us evaluate the gain and the input and output impedances of this amplifier. The open-loop voltage gain of the first stage is seen to be about 180, whereas that of the second stage is about 220 [equation (7.10)]. The low input impedance of the second stage reduces the gain of the first stage to about 50, so the overall open-loop

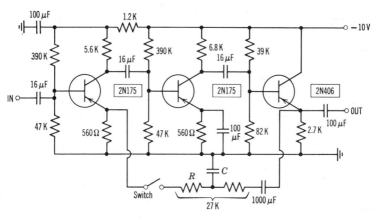

Fig. 7.7 Transistor amplifier with feedback over several stages (2N175, $\beta = 65$; 2N406, $\beta = 50$).

gain A is about 10,400. With the switch closed we have $\phi = -0.0204$, and $1 - \phi A = 212$, so the final gain A' is 49. The output impedance of the second stage is provided by the 6.8 K collector load in parallel with the collector resistance $\partial V_{ce}/\partial i_c$ of the transistor, which is about 40 K, giving a value of 5.8 K. This, in series with r_{be}, constitutes the input impedance of the emitter follower, so the output impedance of the amplifier with the loop open is about 150 ohms. Closing the loop reduces this to 0.7 ohm. The input impedance with the loop open and neglecting feedback in the first stage would be $r_{be} + 560$ ohms, or about 2 K. Closing the loop increases this to 400 K. The actual input impedance is therefore provided mainly by the bias resistor of 47 K, which is quite a respectable value for a transistor amplifier. The amplifier gain could usefully be varied over a range by using a rotary switch to select particular values of the feedback resistor between 5.6 and 56 K, corresponding to values of gain between 10 and 100.

The transistors in Fig. 7.7 are suitable for amplifying signals in the audio-frequency range. Near the upper end of this range the phase shift within the transistors may be sufficient for positive feedback to result, and the *RC* filter network is intended to prevent high-frequency signals from being fed back (typically $R = 5.6$ K,

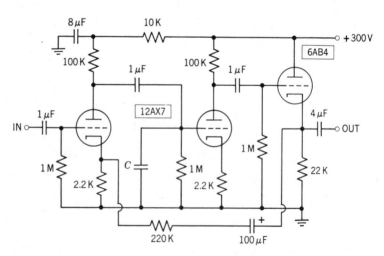

Fig. 7.8   Tube amplifier with feedback over several stages.

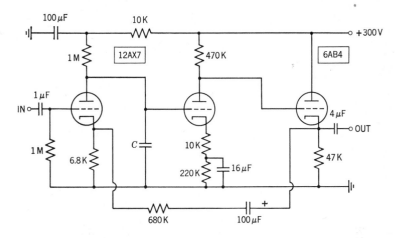

Fig. 7.9 Direct-coupled modification of the amplifier of Fig. 7.8.

$C = 0.0056$ μF). Persistent trouble from this source can be eliminated by inserting a small capacitor (say, 1000 pF) between the base of the second transistor and earth so as to reduce the open-loop gain at high frequencies. The load on the amplifier should be primarily resistive, for otherwise an undesirable phase shift may occur within the emitter follower.

An analogous tube amplifier is shown in Fig. 7.8. The gain of the first stage with the loop open is 55, and that of the second stage about 45 (there is some local feedback in this stage). With the loop closed the overall gain is 96. The capacitor C, which may be about 390 pF, is included if it is necessary to reduce the open-loop gain at high frequencies. The phase shift which occurs in the coupling capacitors at very low frequencies can be avoided if necessary by using direct coupling, as in the circuit of Fig. 7.9. In this circuit the open-loop gain is about 4000, and with the loop closed the gain is 98.

In recent years a number of ingenious circuits have been designed to exploit the capabilities of feedback in combination with *operational amplifiers*. An operational amplifier (Fig. 7.10) is simply a voltage amplifier with a differential input (cf. the long-tailed pair, Chapter 5) and very high open-loop gain. By means of appropriate feedback loops it is possible to make an operational amplifier function as an oscillator, switch, amplifier, differentiator, integrator, voltage

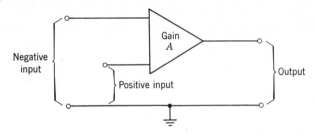

Fig. 7.10   Operational amplifier symbol.

standard, constant-current source, etc. Because of limitations of space we shall not deal with operational amplifiers here, although some of the applications are described in general terms in the appropriate sections. For further information the reader is referred to the literature.[5]

7d   FEEDBACK AND TUNED AMPLIFIERS

At high frequencies it is relatively easy to use tuned circuits to provide selective amplifier response at any desired frequency. In the audio-frequency range, however, and especially near the lower end of this range, it is not convenient to employ tuned circuits because the values of inductance and capacitance which are required become very large. In this case the best way to construct a tuned amplifier is to make use of negative feedback and selective RC networks, such as the twin-T network described in Chapter 1.

A simple feedback circuit using the twin-T network is shown in Fig. 7.11. It will be recalled that the network does not allow any signal of frequency $f = 1/2\pi RC$ to pass, but other frequencies do penetrate, and in the circuit of Fig. 7.11 they will be fed back to the control grid in such a way that the amplifier gain is reduced. In the derivation of the twin-T formula it was necessary to assume that the output worked into a very high impedance; therefore this type of selective amplifier could not be constructed very easily on the basis of a transistor in the common-emitter configuration. For

[5] For example, C. F. Morrison, *Generalized instrumentation for research and teaching.* Pullman: Washington State University, 1964.

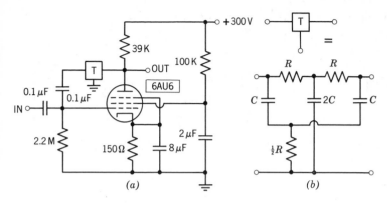

Fig. 7.11 (a) Selective amplifier using feedback over one stage, (b) twin-T network; for 500 cycles/sec $R = 68$ K, $C = 0.047$ μF.

the circuit of Fig. 7.11 it is necessary that the output impedance of the signal source should be of the order of one megohm or more. A typical application would be as a selective amplifier for the output from a vacuum photocell (Fig. 7.12), such as would be required as the first stage in producing a reference signal for a phase-sensitive detector.

A second type of tuned amplifier, shown in Fig. 7.13, is based on the untuned amplifier of Fig. 7.9. Here one feedback loop is used

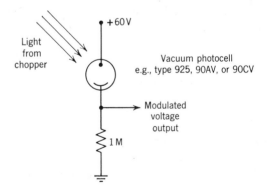

Fig. 7.12 A suitable input for the amplifier of Fig. 7.11.

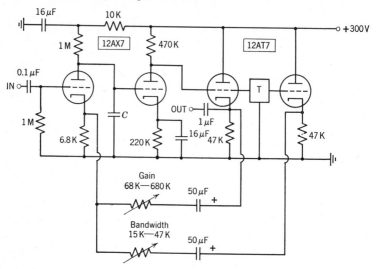

Fig. 7.13 Tuned audio-frequency amplifier. $\boxed{T}$ = twin-T network. Cf. Fig. 10.3.

to control the gain at the desired frequency, and a second loop is used to reduce the gain at other frequencies. Other variants of this type of circuit may be found in the literature.[6] Similar amplifiers, in which the twin-T network operates into the high impedance of an emitter-follower stage, can be designed without too much difficulty (cf. Exercise 7.2). The underlying principle, that of applying a large amount of negative feedback by way of a twin-T network operating into a high impedance, is obviously capable of wide application.

7e REGULATED POWER SUPPLIES

A regulated power supply forms an essential, if inconspicuous, part of practically every electronic instrument that is likely to be encountered in the laboratory. Only in very critical low-hum (i.e., low residual ripple) applications, or in situations where compactness and portability are primary considerations, are chemical batteries likely to be preferred. In most instances the variability of the load,

[6] For example, T. J. Seed, *Review of Scientific Instruments*, **35**, 473 (1964).

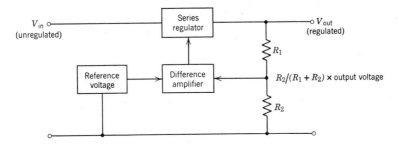

Fig. 7.14 Block diagram of a regulated power supply.

or the requirement of stability under varying loads, is such that simple voltage regulators using Zener diodes or voltage regulator tubes are inadequate, and it is necessary to use negative feedback to provide a stable output.

The essential features of a regulated power supply are shown in Fig. 7.14. In this circuit the difference between a portion of the output voltage and some standard reference voltage is amplified and used to control the current through a *series regulator*, which may be a power tube or power transistor, in such a way that the difference signal is minimized. The reference voltage is usually supplied by either a Zener diode or a voltage regulator tube, although a battery or standard cell can be used.

A circuit for obtaining a regulated output voltage with the aid of vacuum tubes is given in Fig. 7.15. We can analyze the performance of this circuit as follows. Assume $i \gg i'$. Then for the series regulator

$$di = \frac{dv_a}{\rho} + g_m \, dv_g$$

i.e.,

$$\rho \, di = (dV_{in} - dV_{out}) - \mu R \, di' \qquad (7.14)$$

and for the difference amplifier, assuming this to be either a pentode or a cascode amplifier,

$$di' = g'_m \, dv'_g$$
$$= g'_m k \, dV_{out} \qquad (7.15)$$

where

$$V_{out} = iR_L \qquad (7.16)$$

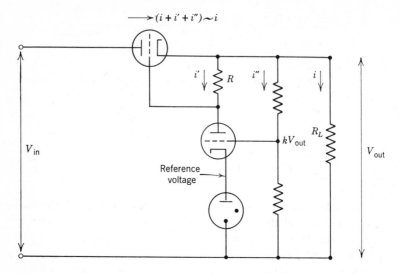

Fig. 7.15   Voltage regulator using vacuum tubes.

Since the aim of the circuit is to make the output voltage independent of both the input voltage and the output current, the important quantities for describing the performance of the circuit are the stabilization factor $(\partial V_{\text{out}}/\partial V_{\text{in}})_{R_L}$ and the output impedance $(\partial V_{\text{out}}/\partial i)_{V_{\text{in}}}$, and both of these should be as small as possible. With R_L constant equation (7.16) gives

$$dV_{\text{out}} = di R_L \qquad (7.17)$$

and (7.14), (7.15), and (7.17) together yield

$$\left(\frac{\partial V_{\text{out}}}{\partial V_{\text{in}}}\right)_{R_L} = \frac{R_L}{\rho + R_L + k\mu R_L g_m' R} \qquad (7.18)$$

$$= \frac{R_L}{\rho + R_L + k\mu R_L A''} \qquad (7.19)$$

where A'' is the voltage gain of the difference amplifier. It is usually a good approximation to simplify this to

$$\left(\frac{\partial V_{\text{out}}}{\partial V_{\text{in}}}\right)_{R_L} = \frac{1}{k\mu A''} \qquad (7.20)$$

At constant input voltage equation (7.14) becomes

$$\rho \, di = -dV_{\text{out}}(1 + k\mu g_m' R) \qquad (7.21)$$

or

$$\left(\frac{\partial V_{\text{out}}}{\partial i}\right)_{V_{\text{in}}} = -\frac{\rho}{1 + k\mu A''}$$

$$= -\frac{\rho}{k\mu A''} \qquad (7.22)$$

approximately.

A practical circuit of this type is shown in Fig. 7.16. The series regulator is a Mullard 6080 double triode, the two sections being used in parallel. This tube is rated to deliver up to 125 mA from each section. The value of R is chosen to give the correct grid voltage at the expected operating point; here, with $V_{\text{in}} - V_{\text{out}}$ in the neighborhood of 150 V, the grid voltage needs to vary from -60 to -90 V as the total output current varies from 150 mA down to zero. Other tubes which are commonly used as series regulators are the Ediswan 12E1, and RCA 2A3, 6L6, or 6V6 (it is usually necessary to use two tubes in parallel except in the case of the 12E1). The 220 ohm resistors in the anode circuits of the 6080 are to help equalize the loads on the sections when they are operating near maximum output. The resistors in series with the grid leads are customarily inserted as insurance against instability. The 1 μF capacitor in the regulator circuit takes any ripple in the output directly to the control grid of the difference amplifier without attenuation by the potential divider. The output voltage can be varied over a small range by means of the 10 K potentiometer in the potential divider. The current through the 12AX7 cascode amplifier is at most 0.5 mA, so the rest of the burning current of the 85A2 voltage reference tube must flow through the 47 K resistor.

For the components in Fig. 7.16 we find $\mu = 2.0$ and $\rho = 300$ ohms for each section, and $R = 180$ K, $R_L = 2$ K or more, $g_m' = 1.25$ mA/V, and $k = 0.283$. With the two 6080 sections in parallel we still have $\mu = 2.0$, but now $\rho = 150$ ohms only. In series with this resistance we have to include the two 220 ohm resistors in parallel, the 220 ohm limiting resistor, and such odds and ends as the dc resistances of the transformer winding and the choke, so the effective

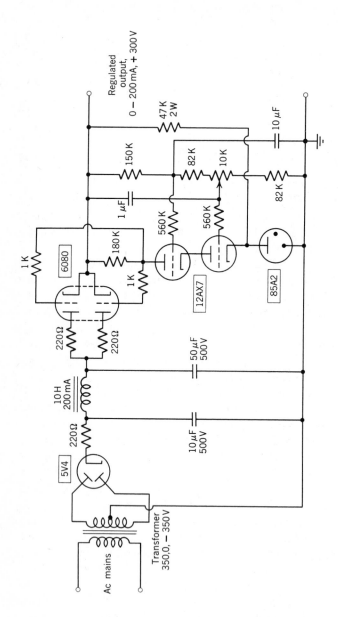

Fig. 7.16   Practical 300 V supply using vacuum tubes.

ρ is about 600 ohms. The gain A'' works out to be 225. Hence, from equations (7.20) and (7.22),

$$\left(\frac{\partial V_{\text{out}}}{\partial V_{\text{in}}}\right)_{R_L} = \frac{1}{127}$$

and

$$\left(\frac{\partial V_{\text{out}}}{\partial i}\right)_{V_{\text{in}}} = 5 \text{ ohms}$$

Many other variants of this type of circuit may be found in the literature.[7] The one given here is a useful laboratory workhorse.

For very high voltages (roughly 2500 V and above), where only a small current is to be delivered, the commonest procedure is to use an oscillator to produce a radio-frequency signal, at about 100 kc, whose amplitude is stabilized, and to employ an rf transformer to step up this amplitude to several thousand volts. The stepped-up signal is then rectified and smoothed, quite small smoothing capacitors being sufficient for peak rectification because of the high frequency. Voltage doublers and treblers (Exercise 6.3) can also be usefully incorporated into this type of power supply. For further details see reference 5 in the list at the end of this chapter.

A very simple power supply which uses a transistor as a series regulator is shown in Fig. 7.17. In this circuit the output voltage is equal to the voltage across the Zener diode plus the emitter-base

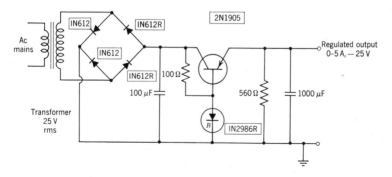

Fig. 7.17   Simple regulated supply using transistors.

[7] See C. R. McKinney et al., *Review of Scientific Instruments*, **21**, 724 (1950).

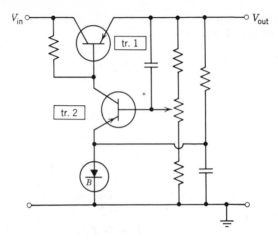

Fig. 7.18   Transistor voltage regulator incorporating a
difference amplifier.

voltage of the transistor.   Part of the Zener diode current flows into
the base of the series transistor and the remainder flows through the
220 ohm resistor.   The purpose of the 560 ohm resistor is to ensure
that the current through the series regulator does not decrease to the
point at which β begins to fall off markedly.   It is important to note
that as the emitter-base voltage of the transistor rises with increasing
load current, so tending to decrease the output voltage, the Zener
diode voltage also rises, so tending to increase the output voltage,
and the achievement of a very low output impedance depends on
careful matching of the characteristics of the transistor and the Zener
diode.   The temperature coefficients of the semiconductor parameters also need to be taken into account, and the maximum permissible ambient temperature during operation (typically 70°C) is
limited by the decrease in the permissible dissipation in the series
transistor with increasing temperature.

In Fig. 7.18 a simple method of incorporating a difference amplifier
into a transistorized power supply is shown.   The regulation and
current output can be improved by using the Darlington configuration for transistor 1 or transistor 2, or both.   The evaluation of the
performance of this power supply is left as an exercise for the reader
(Exercise 7.4).   It is an advantage if the voltage across the series
regulator can be kept low because the power dissipation in this
transistor can give rise to serious cooling problems.   Circuits have

been designed which use a silicon-controlled rectifier to control the
voltage across the series transistor.   In these circuits the input to the
reservoir capacitor is turned off until the voltage across the series
transistor falls below some predetermined value, when the SCR fires
and allows the charge on the capacitor to build up again.   This
arrangement confers an additional advantage in that it enables the
power supply to handle very large variations of input voltage.

Sometimes it is desirable to have a power supply which will deliver
a constant current, rather than a constant voltage, as for example in
the moving boundary experiment for measuring transport number.
Either a pentode (or cascode amplifier) or a transistor can function
as a useful constant-current generator, because the current is determined by the bias voltage on the grid or base in conjunction with the
cathode or emitter resistor and is hardly affected by variations in the
plate or collector voltage.   Two simple constant-current supplies are
shown in Fig. 7.19.   In each case, because of the feedback which

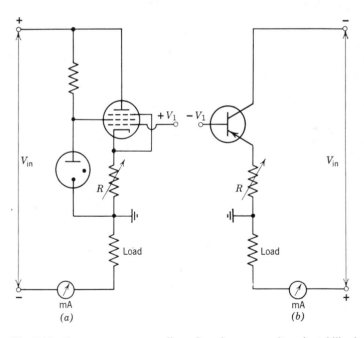

Fig. 7.19   Constant current supplies.   In *a* the screen voltage is stabilized
by means of a voltage reference tube (or Zener diode) connected between
screen grid and cathode.

results from cathode-follower or emitter-follower action, the current delivered is effectively equal to V_1/R. Here V_1 should be large compared with the grid-cathode or base-emitter voltage.

A constant-current supply will deliver a constant voltage if the current is driven through a fixed load. A photomultiplier power supply which uses this principle is shown in Fig. 7.20. In a photomultiplier tube (Fig. 7.21) the incident light strikes a photosensitive surface (the *photocathode*) and ejects electrons which are attracted, by a potential difference of about $+100$ V, to the first *dynode*. When these electrons strike the dynode each one brings about the ejection of five or six secondary electrons, which are in turn attracted to the second dynode, and so on. Typically there are nine dynodes and a final anode, and by the time the anode is reached each initial photoelectron has been multiplied into a shower of 10^5 or 10^6. The requirements of the power supply are that it should provide a negative potential of up to 1000 V for the photocathode, with regular steps of up to 100 V at a time for each of the dynodes. In

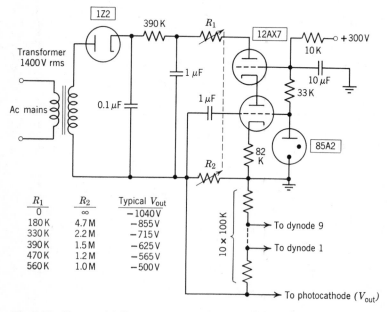

R_1	R_2	Typical V_{out}
0	∞	-1040 V
180 K	4.7 M	-855 V
330 K	2.2 M	-715 V
390 K	1.5 M	-625 V
470 K	1.2 M	-565 V
560 K	1.0 M	-500 V

Fig. 7.20   Photomultiplier power supply (1 mA at 1000 V) based on a constant-current generator.

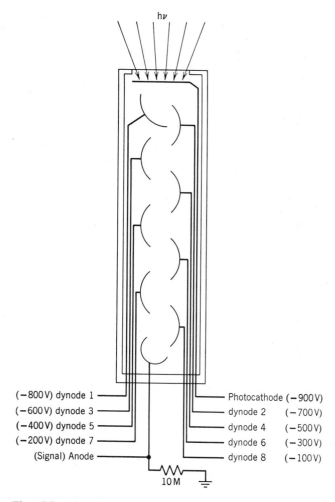

Fig. 7.21 A nine-stage, end-window-type photomultiplier (schematic). The photocathode is made thin enough to be semitransparent.

the circuit of Fig. 7.20 the fixed load is provided by ten 100 K resistors in series, these giving ten equal voltage steps, and the constant-current generator is designed to deliver 1 mA. By introducing a second resistor R_2 in parallel with the 1 M load, the output voltage can be reduced in a controlled fashion. When this is done, a resistance R_1 is inserted as shown in order to keep the voltage drop across the cascode amplifier within reasonable limits. The circuit requires an auxiliary regulated supply of $+250$ V or more to provide the grid voltages for the 12AX7 sections. The lower grid receives its stabilization from the 85A2 tube. Any hum which appears in the output is fed back directly to the current supply by way of the 1 μF capacitor and its amplitude is consequently very much reduced.

Photomultipliers, and to a lesser extent electron multipliers for particle counting are employed in a wide variety of instruments. There are several very good books which deal with the physics of their operation,[8] but probably the best way to obtain a feeling for their behavior in practice, apart from the potentially expensive method of try-it-and-see, is to consult manufacturers' manuals, such as reference 6 in the list at the end of this chapter.

EXERCISES

7.1 Show that the output impedance presented by the anode of a tube, with current feedback from an unbypassed cathode resistor R_k, is given by

$$(\partial V_{\text{out}}/\partial i_a)_{v_{\text{in}}} = \rho + (\mu + 1)R_k$$

(Note that this will be in parallel with the anode load R_L from the point of view of the output signal.)   Derive the corresponding expression for the analogous transistor stage, including allowance for the finite collector resistance $\partial V_{ce}/\partial i_c$ of the transistor. What happens to the input impedance as a result of the feedback?

7.2 Design a transistor amplifier similar to the tuned amplifier of Fig. 7.13. (Base the design on Fig. 7.7 if necessary.) Ensure that the twin-T network (for $f = 500$ cycles, say) operates into an impedance which is at least fifty times the largest impedance in the T.

7.3 The accompanying diagrams 1, 2, and 3 are of feedback amplifiers in which (a) a voltage is fed back to the input as a voltage (cf. Figs. 7.1, 7.7, etc.); (b) a voltage is fed back to the input as a current (cf. Fig. 7.6); (c) a current is fed back as a voltage (cf. Figs. 7.3, 7.4).   In (a) the input impedance is increased and the output impedance decreased; in (b) the input and output impedances are both decreased; and in (c) the input

---

[8] For example, V. K. Zworykin and E. G. Ramberg, *Photoelectricity*. New York: John Wiley & Sons, Inc., 1949.

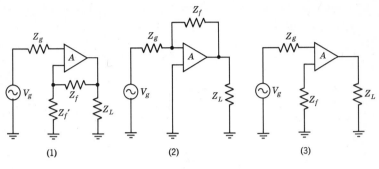

Ex. 7.3

and output impedances are both increased. What would you expect if a current were fed back as a current?

7.4 Why was it really unnecessary to bypass the 47 ohm cathode resistor of the 6AU6 amplifier, designed in section 4b, with a capacitor?

7.5 Analyze the circuit of Fig. 7:18 in the same way that the circuit of Fig. 7.15 was analyzed. (Assume that the base current of transistor 1 is only a very small fraction of the collector current of transistor 2, and that the base current of transistor 2 is small compared with the current through the potential divider to which the base is connected. The results will then be analogous to equations (7.20) and (7.22).) Estimate the improvement in regulation which results from using the Darlington configuration for one or both of the transistors. Try to devise a similar circuit using a long-tailed pair as the difference amplifier.

7.6 Shunt regulators, such as that illustrated below, have the advantage that no harm comes to the regulating transistors if the output terminals are short-circuited. Discuss the mode of operation of this circuit.

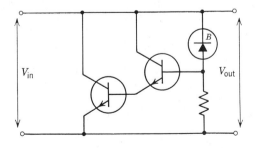

Ex. 7.6

7.7 Show that for the constant-current supply illustrated here

$$dV_{in}/di = (\mu + 1)R_1 + \rho(\mu + 1) + (\rho + R_1 + R_2)$$

Hence evaluate dV_{out}/dV_{in} for the circuit of Fig. 7.20, where $dV_{out} = R_2\,di$.

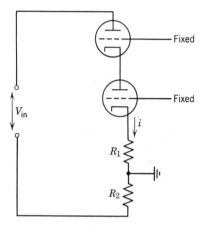

Ex. 7.7

REFERENCES

1. Norbert Wiener, *Cybernetics*. New York: John Wiley & Sons, Inc., 1948.
2. L. B. Arguimbau, *Vacuum-tube circuits and transistors*. New York: John Wiley & Sons, Inc., 1957, Chapter 10.
3. *GE transistor manual*. Syracuse, N.Y.: General Electric Company, Sixth Edition, 1962, Chapter 14.
4. H. V. Malmstadt, C. G. Enke, and E. C. Toren, Jr. *Electronics for scientists*. New York: W. A. Benjamin, 1963, Sections 4.6 and 4.7 and Chapter 8.
5. W. C. Elmore and M. Sands, *Electronics*. New York: McGraw-Hill Book Company, 1949, Chapter 7.
6. *Phototubes and photocells*, RCA Technical Manual PT-60. Lancaster, Pa.: Radio Corporation of America, 1963.
7. D. O. Ward, *Electronic Industries*, May and July issues, 1962. (On regulating and stabilizing high-voltage power supplies.)

8

Limits to Amplification:
Bandwidth and Noise

....

8a INTRODUCTION

In this chapter we shall consider some factors which constitute
fundamental limitations on the performance of tube and transistor
amplifiers. The first of these limitations is the inability of amplifiers
to respond to signals at very high or very low frequencies. So far,
for example in Chapter 4, we have worked in terms of the amplifier
gain at mid-band frequencies, i.e., where this limitation is not
encountered, but our results are of little use unless we are aware of
the frequency range over which they are valid. At the lower end of
the frequency range the limitations are imposed by the coupling
elements in a circuit, since capacitors and transformers are only able
to conduct ac signals. At the upper end of the range the limitations
for a tube amplifier are imposed first by parasitic capacitances and
later by transit-time effects, but for a transistor amplifier the first
limitation is likely to be the rate of diffusion of carriers through the
base, with effects from unwanted capacitances appearing only somewhat later. The factors which limit bandwidth, and some methods
of reducing their effects, are described in section 8b. In all cases the
range of practically constant amplification can obviously be extended,
at the expense of a considerable reduction in mid-band gain, by
introducing negative feedback.

The second major limitation appears when we endeavor to make
an amplifier respond to signals of smaller and smaller amplitude.

169

Once the signals are below a certain size it turns out that they can no longer be detected with certainty because of the presence of various unsuspected signals, collectively termed *noise*, in the output. The two most fundamental sources of this noise are first the circumstance that at all temperatures above absolute zero the electrons in a conductor are in continuous random motion, and second the fact that electrons travel through a vacuum, or through the depletion layer at a *pn* junction, in the form of a hail of discrete particles rather than as a continuous current.   There are many other sources of noise, but these two are inherent in the nature of electricity.   The random motion of electrons in a conductor gives rise to a fluctuating potential difference which is superimposed on the signal that is being measured.   The statistical fluctuations in the rate of arrival of the discrete particles which constitute the current in a tube or transistor are similarly superimposed upon the fluctuations which are due to a small signal applied to the grid or base.   The magnitudes of these and other effects, and the means by which they can be minimized, are discussed in section 8c.

8b   BANDWIDTH

Low-Frequency Limitations.   We shall consider only *RC*-coupled amplifiers, since with transformer coupling the main factor is the design of the transformer, a topic that is outside the scope of this book.

At low frequencies the bandwidth limitations are imposed by interstage coupling capacitors, if any are present, and possibly also by capacitors which are used to bypass cathode or emitter resistors. With direct coupling, as described in Chapter 5, the low-frequency limitation can be made entirely negligible.   To calculate the effect of a coupling capacitor in the general case let us consider Fig. 8.1. At low frequencies the parasitic capacitances, e.g., interelectrode capacitances in tubes or stray wiring capacitances, can be neglected, and the input and output impedances are purely resistive.   The input circuit is seen to be similar to the differentiating network of Chapter 1. Therefore we have, at low frequencies,

$$\frac{V'_{in}}{V_{out}} = \frac{R'_{in}}{R'_{in} + R_{out} - j/\omega C} \tag{8.1}$$

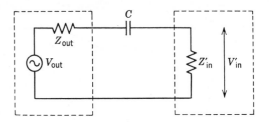

Fig. 8.1 Circuit with limited low-frequency response.

which shows that when $1/\omega C$ is large the input voltage V'_{in} approaches $R'_{in}\omega C V_{out}$, and the phase shift in the coupling network approaches $90°$.

At a mid-band frequency we have

$$\frac{V'_{in}}{V_{out}} = \frac{R'_{in}}{R'_{in} + R_{out}} \tag{8.2}$$

so if A_m and A_f are the overall amplifier gain at a mid-band frequency and at a frequency f, we can write

$$\frac{A_f}{A_m} = \left(1 - \frac{j}{\omega CR}\right)^{-1} = \left(1 - \frac{j}{2\pi f CR}\right)^{-1} \tag{8.3}$$

where $R = R'_{in} + R_{out}$. In terms of measured voltages this becomes

$$\frac{|A_f|}{|A_m|} = \left(1 + \frac{1}{4\pi^2 f^2 C^2 R^2}\right)^{-\frac{1}{2}} \tag{8.4}$$

The half-power point (often stated as the frequency at which the output power is 3 decibels down from the mid-band value) is therefore given by

$$2\pi f_1 CR = 1 \tag{8.5}$$

The lower half-power frequency is given the symbol f_1. In terms of f_1 equation (8.4) now becomes

$$\frac{|A_f|}{|A_m|} = \left(1 + \frac{f_1^2}{f^2}\right)^{-\frac{1}{2}} \tag{8.6}$$

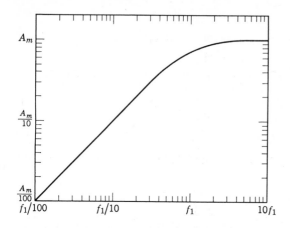

Fig. 8.2   Low-frequency response of an *RC*-coupled amplifier, where the response is limited by the size of the coupling capacitors.

Hence, using f_1 as a reference frequency, we can describe the low-frequency performance of any *RC*-coupled amplifier by means of equation (8.6).   This result is shown graphically in Fig. 8.2.

The low-frequency response of an *RC*-coupled amplifier can be improved by one of the compensation methods that are illustrated in Fig. 8.3.   These depend on increasing the amplifier gain at low frequencies in order to compensate for attenuation in the coupling network.   Adjusting the R and L or C values in the compensating networks is to some extent an empirical art, and care must be taken to avoid overcompensation, which can give rise to a peak at the low-frequency end of the response curve.   In this way an improvement of up to a factor of 2 in f_1 can be obtained.   Obviously, if the best low-frequency response is required, we should omit the coupling capacitors altogether and build a dc amplifier.

By means of equation (8.5) we can calculate f_1 values for the amplifiers which were designed in Chapter 4.   For the pentode amplifier of section 4b we had $R_{out} = 22$ K and $C = 0.1 \, \mu$F.   It can be assumed that this amplifier would normally operate into an impedance R'_{in} of at least 500 K, in which case f_1 works out to be about 3 cycles/sec.   For the grounded-emitter amplifier of section 4c

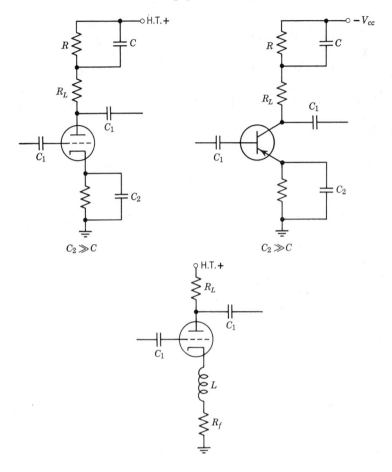

Fig. 8.3   Circuits with low-frequency compensation.

we had $R_{\text{out}} = 4.2$ K and C = 4 μF.   Assuming R'_{in} to be about 2 K (e.g., another common-emitter stage) equation (8.5) gives $f_1 = 6$ cycles/sec.   In this case, however, the low-frequency performance turns out to be limited mainly by the 100 μF bypass capacitor on the emitter resistor.   If the impedance of this capacitor is Z_C, the gain of the amplifier tends to $-R_L/Z_C$ as Z_C increases (cf. section 7b). The mid-band gain was calculated to be -70, so the gain at the half-power frequency is -50.   This corresponds to $Z_C = 84$ ohms, which is the impedance of the 100 μF capacitor at a frequency of 19 cycles/sec. In this instance the response is no longer described by equation (8.6), but the difference is not very important in practice.

For the grounded-grid and common-base amplifiers of sections 4d and 4e the coupling arrangements were not specified, but in any case the lower frequency limit is not likely to be of critical importance because the main applications of these circuits occur at relatively high frequencies. For the cathode-follower and emitter-follower stages of sections 4f and 4g the value of R_{out} was calculated to 240 ohms and 30 ohms, respectively. Assuming that these circuits operate into matching input impedances, the coupling capacitor required for $f_1 = 20$ cycles/sec is 15 μF in the first case and 120 μF in the second. We should note here that if the coupling capacitor is physically large, because of the need for a high voltage rating, the stray capacitances to ground which are thereby introduced will have an adverse effect on the performance of the amplifier at high frequencies. With large electrolytic capacitors the parasitic inductance of the leads can also affect high-frequency performance. To overcome this effect a small ceramic capacitor is commonly connected in parallel with any large bypass capacitor in wide-band applications.

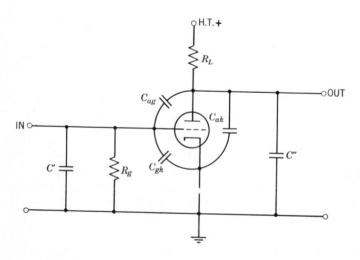

Fig. 8.4   Parasitic and stray capacitances in a triode amplifier.

Tube Amplifiers at High Frequencies.   The high-frequency circuit of a tube amplifier is shown in Fig. 8.4. Here we include stray wiring capacitances and interelectrode capacitances in the tube, but not the parasitic inductances of the connecting wires. These inductances increase the output impedance, and in the case of the inductance of the cathode connection in a grounded-cathode or grounded-grid stage, lead directly to loss of gain. They are normally minimized by careful *lead dress*, i.e., by keeping all high-frequency leads as short and as well separated as possible.

Values of the interelectrode capacitances in several tubes are given in Table 8.1. The wiring capacitances C' and C'' of Fig. 8.4 are usually 10 to 20 pF, or more, depending on how much care is taken over planning the layout of the amplifier.

Table 8.1   Interelectrode Capacitances

Values expressed in picofarads.

Capacitance:	Triode (12AX7 section)	Triode (6A B4)	Pentode (6AU6)
C_{ag}	2.0	1.5 (1.8*)	0.0035
C_{gk}	2.2	2.2 (4.6*)	5.5†
C_{ak}	0.8	0.4 (0.2*)	5.0†

* Grounded-grid configuration.
† Includes heater, grids 2 and 3, and internal shield.

First we consider the effects of the interelectrode capacitances on the input impedance.   In Fig. 8.5 let electrode 1 be the input electrode

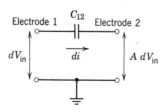

Fig. 8.5 Influence of amplifier gain on effective interelectrode capacitance.

and let the gain to electrode 2 be A. Then if the input signal is dV_{in}, the current which flows through the interelectrode capacitance is given by

$$di = dV_{in}(1 - A)j\omega C_{12} \qquad (8.7)$$

Therefore the *effective* capacitance is equal to $(1 - A)C_{12}$, and the effect of a particular interelectrode capacitance depends on the configuration in which the tube is being used.

To consider some examples, in a common-cathode stage (Fig. 8.4) the gain to the cathode is zero, so that the value of C_{gk} is simply added to C', the capacitance produced by the wiring. The gain to the anode, however, is large and negative, so that the effective size of the capacitance C_{ag} is multiplied by a factor of 100 or more. Not only can this have a very adverse effect on the input impedance, but it can also provide an unwanted feedback path between input and output ("Miller effect"), as mentioned in Chapter 7. The very small value of the capacitance linking the input and output circuits gives the pentode, and also the cascode amplifier, a considerable advantage over a triode for high-frequency applications. Table 8.2 contains values of interelectrode capacitance, total effective input capacitance, and input impedance produced by this capacitance at 10 kc/sec and 10 Mc/sec, for representative triode and pentode amplifiers in the grounded-cathode configuration, and for the cascode amplifier which was described in section 5b. It is apparent that even in the most favorable cases the input impedance at 10 Mc is quite low, and it is partly for this reason that wide-band amplifiers generally obtain a large overall gain by using many stages with quite low values

Table 8.2   Input Impedances due to Interelectrode Capacitances
Values expressed in picofarads.

Tube	R_L	A	C_{ag}	$(1 - A)C_{ag}$	C_{gk}	C_{in}	$Z_{in}(10 \text{ kc})$	$Z_{in}(10 \text{ Mc})$
12AU7	33 K	−16.5	1.5	25	1.6	27	590 K	590 ohms
12AT7	68 K	−55	1.5	84	2.2	86	185 K	185 ohms
12AX7	330 K	−80	2.0	162	2.2	164	97 K	97 ohms
6AU6	22 K	−100	0.0035	0.35	5.5	5.9	2.7 M	2.7 K
12AT7	33 K	−140	1.5	6.3	2.2	8.5	1.9 M	1.9 K
cascode		(−3.2 to a_1)						

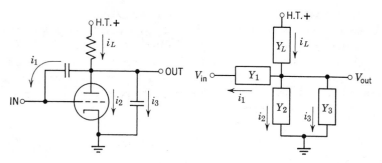

Fig. 8.6   Currents and admittances in an amplifier at high frequencies.

of load resistance, and correspondingly low output impedance (cf. the integrating network, Chapter 1).

In a grounded-grid stage the input impedance is already low and the contribution from the interelectrode capacitance is quite insignificant.   In a cathode-follower stage the gain to the anode is zero and C_{ag} merely adds its contribution to the wiring capacitances.   The gain A is positive and only slightly different from unity, so that the effect of C_{gk} is very greatly reduced.   It follows that the high input impedance of a cathode follower is to a large extent retained at high frequencies.

To evaluate the gain of a common-cathode amplifier at high frequencies we refer to Fig. 8.6.   It will be convenient to work in terms of admittances Y rather than impedances Z, where $Y = 1/Z$, and we note that Y_2 is the same as g_a, i.e., it is simply $1/\rho$ for the tube.   We observe that, by Kirchhoff's first law,

$$di_L = di_1 + di_2 + di_3 \tag{8.8}$$

where
$$di_1 = Y_1(dv_a - dv_g) \tag{8.9}$$

$$di_2 = \frac{dv_a}{\rho} + g_m \, dv_g \tag{8.10}$$

$$= Y_2(dv_a + \mu \, dv_g) \tag{8.11}$$

and
$$di_3 = Y_3 \, dv_a \tag{8.12}$$

Hence
$$\frac{dv_a}{dv_g} = A = - \frac{g_m - Y_1}{Y_L + Y_1 + Y_2 + Y_3} \tag{8.13}$$

This expression reduces to the normal formula for the gain when Y_1 and Y_3 are set equal to zero and Y_L and Y_2 are replaced by $1/R_L$ and $1/\rho$, respectively. For the tubes of Table 8.2 the admittance of C_{ag} does not become equal to g_m until a frequency of about 100 Mc is reached. The effects of Y_1 and Y_3 in the denominator become important at much lower frequencies than this, so it is a good approximation to write,

$$A = -\frac{g_m}{Y_L + Y_1 + Y_2 + Y_3} \qquad (8.14)$$

A second reason for using small values of load resistance in wide-band amplifiers is now apparent, namely, to make Y_L large in comparison with Y_1 and Y_3 over as wide a range of frequencies as possible.

Equation (8.14) can be rewritten in the form

$$A = -\frac{g_m R}{1 + j\omega RC} \qquad (8.15)$$

where

$$\frac{1}{R} = Y_L + Y_2 \qquad (8.16)$$

and

$$j\omega C = Y_1 + Y_3$$

i.e.,

$$C = C_{ag} + C'' + C_{ak} \qquad (8.17)$$

In terms of measured voltages equation (8.15) becomes

$$|A| = -\frac{g_m R}{(1 + 4\pi^2 f^2 R^2 C^2)^{1/2}} \qquad (8.18)$$

The upper half-power frequency is therefore given by

$$f_2 = \frac{1}{2\pi RC} \qquad (8.19)$$

and the gain at any other frequency at the high-frequency end of the band is given by

$$\frac{|A_f|}{|A_m|} = \left(1 + \frac{f^2}{f_2^2}\right)^{-1/2} \qquad (8.20)$$

(since $|A_m| = -g_m R$).

This result is shown graphically in Fig. 8.7. It may be combined with the previous result for the lower end of the band to yield the complete response curve of Fig. 8.8.

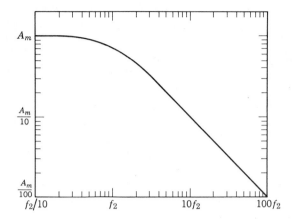

Fig. 8.7 High-frequency response of an amplifier, where the response is limited by parasitic and stray capacitance in parallel with the load.

For the 6AU6 amplifier of section 4b, assuming C'' to be 10 pF, equation (8.19) yields $f_2 = 480$ kc. For the cascode amplifier of section 5b, with the same value of C'', we find $f_2 = 430$ kc. The form of the result (8.19) shows that we can increase the bandwidth by decreasing R, i.e., only at the expense of suffering a reduction in gain, and in fact it is not difficult to show that the gain-bandwidth

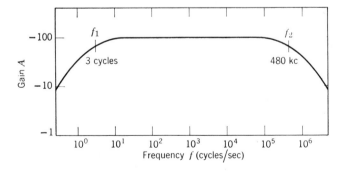

Fig. 8.8 Response curve for 6AU6 amplifier of section 4b, assuming stray wiring capacitance in parallel with the load totals 10 pF, and input resistance of the following stage equals 500 K.

product is a figure of merit for the tube itself (Exercise 8.2).   In this instance it appears that the cascode stage is superior to the pentode, the gain-bandwidth product being 60 Mc in the one case and 48 Mc in the other.   If C'' were zero this superiority would be much more marked.   In a multistage amplifier the performance of one stage is, of course, affected by the input impedance of the following one, and a further point is that the overall bandwidth for several stages is likely to be appreciably worse than that of the worst individual stage.

Two methods of improving the response of an amplifier stage at high frequencies are shown in Fig. 8.9.   As with low-frequency compensation, it is important not to overcompensate because this can cause the formation of a peak at the high-frequency end of the response curve.   In the case of inductive compensation (Fig. 8.9a) the greatest bandwidth (1.7f_2), combined with virtually flat frequency response, is obtained by choosing $L = 0.414R^2C$.

Usually, with tube amplifiers, the limitations which result from the unwanted capacitance are encountered before those due to transit-time effects, which become serious at about 100 Mc.   At high

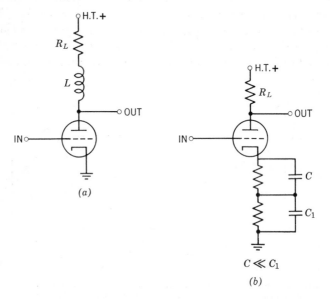

Fig. 8.9   Circuits with high-frequency compensation.

frequencies the input is, roughly speaking, averaged over the time for which the electrons are under the influence of the grid. As mentioned in Chapter 4 (and in Exercise 8.1) the grounded-grid amplifier is superior to other configurations at high frequencies, and in fact special tubes, known as *disk-seal* triodes, have been designed for use as grounded-grid amplifiers at frequencies near 1000 Mc. In these tubes the interelectrode spacings are kept down to about 0.01 of an inch in order to reduce the transit time to a minimum, and their mode of construction enables them to be used with in-line connections so that the effects of lead inductance are also minimized. At frequencies of 1000 Mc and above we have entered the domain of klystrons, magnetrons, masers, and traveling wave tubes, and these, though fascinating, are outside the scope of this book.

Transistor Amplifiers at High Frequencies. The stray capacitances which must be included in the analysis of the performance of a transistor amplifier stage at high frequencies are shown in Fig. 8.10, and their effects can be evaluated in the same manner as the effects of interelectrode capacitances in tubes. However, except with special high-frequency transistors, for example Mullard OC170 ($f_\alpha = 70$ Mc), RCA 2N1177 ($f_\alpha = 140$ Mc), or Texas Instruments 2N2999 ($f_T = 1500$ Mc), the effects of these capacitances are much less important than are transit-time effects within the transistor. This is so, first because of the low impedances which are characteristic of transistor circuits and second because of the lower frequencies (compared with tubes) at which transit-time effects appear.

The internal limitations of a transistor, which result mainly from the finite time that is required for current carriers to diffuse through the base region, are usually expressed in terms of the value of f_α ($= f_{hfb}$), this being the frequency at which α has fallen to 0.707 of the mid-band value.[1] This value gives a good indication of the upper half-power frequency for a common-base stage, since in this case we have approximately

$$A = \alpha Z_{out}/Z_{in} \qquad (8.21)$$

[1] An alternative cutoff frequency, which is easier to measure than f_α, is f_1, the frequency at which β is reduced to unity. This is now quoted in preference to f_α by many manufacturers. For many alloy transistors $f_1 \sim 1.2f_\alpha$. The gain-bandwidth product f_T is equal to f_1 in the common-emitter configuration.

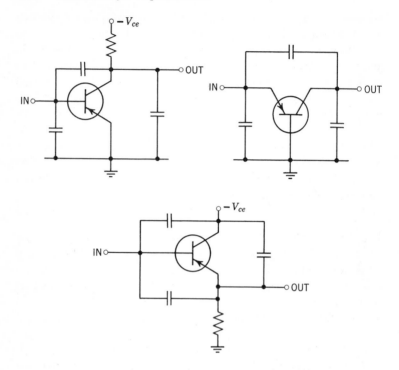

Fig. 8.10   Parasitic capacitances in transistor amplifiers.

(cf. equation 4.23).   For a common-emitter stage the gain obviously
falls off at a much lower frequency because it is proportional to
$\beta = \alpha/(1 - \alpha)$, where α is close to unity at mid-band frequencies.
It can be shown that to a good approximation the upper half-power
frequency of a common-emitter amplifier is given by

$$f_2 = (1 - \alpha)f_\alpha \tag{8.22}$$

where α has its low-frequency value and stray capacitance is assumed
to be negligible.   For the 2N175 amplifier of section 4c the value of
f_α is listed as 0.85 Mc.   Here $\beta = 65$, so $(1 - \alpha) = 1/66$ and
$f_2 = 120$ kc.

The performance of a transistor as a high-speed switch is obviously
related to its high-frequency response as an amplifier; however, there
are also other factors involved and it appears best to postpone their

discussion until Chapter 9, which deals specifically with oscillators and switching circuits.

8c NOISE

The twelve most important kinds of unwanted signals in electronic equipment can be listed as follows.

1. Electromagnetic pickup from extraneous sources, due to poor shielding or to the transmission of switching surges along power lines.

2. Mains hum, due to incomplete smoothing of dc power supplies, poor shielding or pickup from the ac leads to tube filaments.

3. Instability, due to unwanted interactions between different parts of a circuit, or to negative feedback changing to positive feedback in a particular frequency range.

4. Intermittent signals, due to noisy or defective resistors and capacitors, badly soldered connections, or insulation breakdown.

5. Microphonics, due to external vibrations affecting the inter-electrode spacings in tubes.

6. Variations in tube gain, due to changes in the cathode temperature following fluctuations in the filament supply voltage, this voltage usually being unregulated.

7. Thermal noise due to the random motion of electrons in a conductor.

8. Shot noise, due to electrons arriving at the anode of a tube or crossing the depletion layers in a transistor, in the form of a hail of separate particles.

9. Flicker-effect noise in tubes, due to random fluctuations in the rate of evaporation of electrons from the cathode as a result of variations in the nature of the emissive surface.

10. Excess noise, or $1/f$ noise, in transistors, due possibly to fluctuations in the conductivity of the medium (closely related to flicker-effect noise and contact noise).

11. Partition noise, due to random fluctuations in the division of current between two or more electrodes in multigrid tubes.

12. Induced grid noise, due to electrons which pass close to the control grid of a tube inducing a current in the grid-cathode circuit. This induced current appears as an amplified voltage in the anode circuit.

Some of the known sources of noise have been omitted from this list, and probably a few remain to be discovered, but these are the most important ones.

The first six noise sources in the list can all be made negligible if sufficient care is taken. Thus in (1) the unwanted signals can be kept out by means of adequate shielding and decoupling, and by keeping leads which may carry large current surges as short as possible. In (2) the mains hum can be reduced by using a power supply with better smoothing, by improving the overall shielding, and by using a better layout of the heater leads (it is good practice to twist heater leads together so that their effect at a distance is minimized). In critical applications battery supplies can be used throughout. In (3) the instability can usually be countered by arranging for better decoupling of amplifier stages, by keeping sensitive grid and base leads very short, by changing the layout of the circuit to reduce interaction, and by introducing suitable *RC*-filter networks to reduce the gain at frequencies where positive feedback is possible. The intermittent signals in (4) can be disposed of by locating and eliminating faulty components, bad (especially "dry") joints, and poor insulation. Microphonics, item (5) in the list, are usually negligible with transistors and can be virtually eliminated with tubes by using shock-absorber-type mountings and special-quality tubes. The variations in tube gain mentioned in (6) can give rise to serious drifts in dc amplifiers and electrometers, and to similar but more subtle effects in ac amplifiers. The solution is to regulate the filament supply or once more to resort to batteries. Where batteries are used they should preferably be mercury cells to avoid errors from gradually changing e.m.f. during the life of the batteries.

The other six sources of noise are more fundamental. It can be shown, by means of a thermodynamic argument, that *thermal noise*, or *Johnson noise*, is described by the formula

$$\bar{v}^2 = 4kTR\,\varDelta f \tag{8.23}$$

or the equivalent expression

$$\bar{i}^2 = 4kTY\,\varDelta f \tag{8.24}$$

where $\bar{v}^2$ is the mean-square voltage of the effective voltage generator (Fig. 8.11a), $\bar{i}^2$ is the mean-square current of the equivalent current

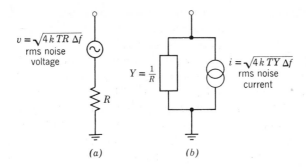

Fig. 8.11 Thermal noise: equivalent rms voltage and current sources.

generator (Fig. 8.11b), k is Boltzmann's constant (1.38×10^{-23} joule/°K), T is the absolute temperature, R is the resistance in which the noise is developed, $Y (= 1/R)$ is the corresponding conductance, and Δf is the width of the frequency band in which the noise is measured.[1] For $R = 10^6$ ohms, $T = 300°$K, and $\Delta f = 10$ kc we find that the rms (root-mean-square) value of noise voltage is 13 μV, corresponding to an rms current of 1.3×10^{-11} ampere.

Shot noise in tubes is described by the formula

$$\bar{i}^2 = 2I\epsilon\Gamma^2 \, \Delta f \tag{8.25}$$

where $\bar{i}^2$ and Δf have the same significance as before, ϵ is the electronic charge (1.60×10^{-19} coulomb), I is the anode current, and the quantity Γ^2, which typically has a value between 0.05 and 0.3, is known as the "space-charge reduction factor." This factor arises because the electron does not travel through a complete vacuum, but through a region which contains space charge. The interaction with the space charge causes the arrival of electrons at the anode to be less of a random affair than it would be otherwise. In tubes in which secondary electrons can reach the anode the effective value of ϵ is increased and the shot noise may be greater than would be expected from equation (8.25). Thus in a photomultiplier tube,

---

[1] These formulas hold at frequencies for which f is much less than kT/h; outside this range the Planck radiation law takes over. At 300°K the value of kT/h is 6×10^{12} cycles/sec. Electronics, in the guise of *lasers*, is only just in the process of colonizing this spectral region.

where each impulse at the anode consists of a shower of 10^5 or 10^6 electrons, the rms shot noise is increased by a factor of about 10^3. In a triode amplifier for an anode current of 0.2 mA, with $\Gamma^2 = 0.3$ and $\Delta f = 10$ kc, we find the rms shot noise current to be 5×10^{-10} ampere. These figures would be fairly typical of a 12AX7 triode section with an anode load of 1 M. The plate resistance ρ in this case is 100 K, so the resulting rms noise signal in the output is 50 μV, which is equivalent to a signal of 0.5 μV applied to the grid. It is important to remember here that the total effective rms noise signal in the grid is not $\bar{v}_{shot} + \bar{v}_{thermal}$ but $(\bar{v}_{shot}^2 + \bar{v}_{thermal}^2)^{1/2}$, so the effect of the shot noise is very small.

It can be shown that to a good approximation, up to moderately high frequencies, the shot noise in a tube can be represented by a noise generator consisting of an equivalent resistor R_{eq} in series with the control grid, where for a triode

$$R_{eq} = 2.5/g_m \tag{8.26}$$

and, as usual, g_m is the mutual conductance. The effect of shot noise is then equivalent to a mean-square voltage generator

$$\bar{v}^2 = 4.1 \times 10^{-20} \Delta f/g_m \tag{8.27}$$

in series with the control grid. We can now conclude that, for example, a 12AT7 section ($\mu = 60$, $g_m = 4.5$ mA/V) is less noisy than a 12AX7 section ($\mu = 100$, $g_m = 1.2$ mA/V), but in either case if the input to the amplifier is from a high-impedance source, the main source of noise from the amplifier will be thermal noise in the grid resistor, which is typically 10^5 or 10^6 ohms.

The formula (8.25) also describes shot noise in transistors, but in this case the situation is less clear-cut, and it appears best to lump shot noise together with other forms of internal noise, including Johnson noise, and express them all in terms of the "noise figure" of the transistor, as will be described shortly.

Both flicker-effect noise in tubes and excess noise in transistors obey an equation of the form

$$\bar{v}^2 = \text{constant} \times \Delta f/f \tag{8.28}$$

or $$\bar{i}^2 = \text{constant}' \times \Delta f/f \tag{8.29}$$

with quite remarkable accuracy down to frequencies of the order of a small fraction of a cycle per second. At low frequencies this form of noise is predominant, becoming comparable in magnitude with other forms of noise at about 100 cycles/sec with tubes, and at about 1000 cycles/sec with general-purpose transistors. A rigorous theoretical justification of a noise law of this form appears to be very difficult to achieve, partly because the exact physical mechanism by which the noise arises is not well established. One immediate consequence of the existence of $1/f$ noise is that a better signal-to-noise ratio can usually be obtained from a dc amplifier which uses a chopper and subsequent ac amplification than from one which employs strictly dc methods, even though the chopper must introduce its own quota of noise.

Partition noise, caused by random variations in the division of current between anode and screen, is an important source of noise in tetrodes and pentodes. This noise can be minimized by selecting a tube with a large g_m and low screen current, both of which are desirable characteristics for other reasons. The cascode amplifier does not suffer from this form of noise, but it does have the advantages of a pentode for obtaining high gain and for work at frequencies where triodes would give trouble because of the Miller effect. Hence a cascode stage is often to be preferred as the first stage of a low-noise, wide-band amplifier. (We shall see shortly that low-noise requirements are most critical in the first stage of an amplifier.) In the presence of partition noise the shot noise formula (8.26) becomes

$$R_{eq} = \frac{2.5}{g_m} \left(1 + \frac{8i_{g2}}{g_m} \right) \frac{i_a}{i_k} \tag{8.30}$$

where i_a, i_k, and i_{g2} are the anode, cathode, and screen grid currents, respectively. For the 6AU6 amplifier of section 4b we had $g_m = 4.5$ mA/V, $i_a = 7.5$ mA, $i_k = 10.5$ mA, and $i_{g2} = 3$ mA. Hence $R_{eq} = 2.5$ K and the resulting equivalent rms voltage signal at the grid is 0.64 μV, for $\Delta f = 10$ kc. Since the actual bandwidth of this amplifier has just been found to be 480 kc, the rms noise voltage, consisting of shot and partition noise, would amount to the equivalent of 31 μV at the control grid. This may be compared with a calculated figure of 7.2 μV rms produced by shot noise at the control grid of the 12AT7 cascode amplifier of section 5b, whose bandwidth was found to be 430 kc.

Induced grid noise, item 12 on the list of noise sources, is not usually important at frequencies below 100 Mc.

The significant quantity for describing the precision with which information can be obtained from a signal is the *signal-to-noise* ratio, S/N. This is the ratio of the *power* which is available from the signal to the power which is available from its accompanying noise. The *noise figure F*, for any device, is defined as the ratio of S/N in the output signal to S/N in the input signal. If an amplifier contained no internal sources of noise, its noise figure would be unity, or zero decibels. A signal of any kind is invariably accompanied by noise when it first arrives at an electronic device, for example, the light signal which is incident on a phototube already contains a form of shot noise, owing to random fluctuations in the number of individual photons which arrive at the photocathode in a given time interval. If the first stage of an amplifier possesses sufficient gain, the noise introduced by subsequent stages will be negligible in comparison with the amplified noise from the first stage. Therefore it is advisable to make the first stage of a low-noise amplifier one which has the largest possible gain combined with the smallest possible noise figure. The contribution from the noise figures for subsequent stages is given by Friis's formula for the overall noise figure of a multistage device:

$$F = F_1 + \frac{F_2 - 1}{A_1} + \frac{F_3 - 1}{A_1 A_2} + \frac{F_4 - 1}{A_1 A_2 A_3} + \cdots \qquad (8.31)$$

Here $F_1, F_2, F_3, \cdots$ and $A_1, A_2, A_3, \cdots$ are the noise figures and gains for stages 1, 2, 3, etc.

Noise figures are generally listed as so many decibels per unit bandwidth at 1 kc, although "spot noise figures" at other frequencies may also be quoted. The noise figure of a 2N175 transistor (of. section 4c) is listed simply as 6 decibels maximum, which is quite good for a transistor. Tubes can be expected to have much better noise figures than this, usually well below one decibel. With both tubes and transistors the noise figure is virtually independent of amplifier configuration but does vary considerably with frequency, being markedly higher at low frequencies, where $1/f$ noise is important. With transistors there is an optimum value of source impedance, effectively equal to the input impedance of the transistor, such that the noise figure is a minimum, for if the source impedance is very high or very low not much power is transferred from the source to the transistor, but the noise contributed by the transistor itself is essentially constant. The noise contribution from the transistor decreases with decreasing emitter current, provided this is not so low that β has fallen off appreciably, and also with decreasing leakage current. Therefore the first stage of a low-noise transistor amplifier should preferably be a silicon transistor operating at the lowest possible emitter current consistent with maintaining a reasonably large value of β. Some graphs which show the variation of noise figure with frequency, source resistance, and emitter current are given in Fig. 8.12 for an advanced type of silicon transistor.

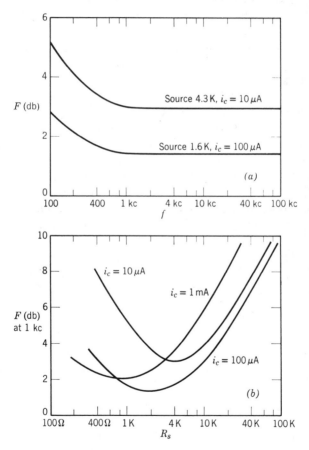

Fig. 8.12 Variation of noise figure with (*a*) frequency and (*b*) source resistance, for a typical high-quality silicon transistor (Motorola *pnp* type 2N3250 or 2N3251).

Field-effect transistors generally have much better noise figures than do ordinary junction transistors, and selected types are comparable with vacuum tubes (e.g., Texas Instruments type 2N2500, for which $F \leqslant 5$ decibels at 10 cycles/sec). The high input impedance of the FET is also valuable in the first stage of an amplifier. The only disadvantage of these devices is that at present their price is several times that of a good silicon junction transistor, but it can reasonably be expected that this situation will improve. An FET low-noise preamplifier (for use with a lead sulfide photoconductor and chopped light source in the near infrared) is illustrated in Fig. 8.13.

The nature of the noise which accompanies the input signal to an amplifier depends on the nature of the transducer which is used to produce the signal. Thus, for example, the output from a photomultiplier tube contains highly developed shot noise, whereas the output from a high-resistance photoconductor (Fig. 8.13) contains the usual thermal noise, with superimposed shot noise produced by the random arrival of individual photons. The ion current signal from a mass spectrometer contains shot noise, due to random arrival of individual ions, plus thermal noise, due to the high-valued resistor which must be used if the very small ion current is to produce an appreciable voltage signal. The output from a Geiger-Müller tube is noisy because the count rate fluctuates as a result of the

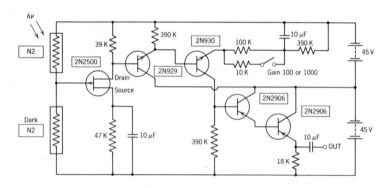

Fig. 8.13 Low-noise preamplifier using an FET input stage. (Photoconductors: Kodak *Ektron* type N2, 2 × 1 cm, dark resistance 200 K, matched pair. Almost any small-signal *pnp* transistor will do for the output stage.)

statical nature of radioactive disintegration, with an extra component of noise being derived from fluctuations in the background count. Whatever the source of noise, however, there are several general conclusions that can be reached in answer to the question of how to obtain the best signal-to-noise ratio in an electrical measurement. These conclusions are as follows:

1. Both tubes and transistors suffer from $1/f$ noise at low frequencies. Therefore the best signal-to-noise ratio will be obtained if the voltage or current which is being measured is chopped before being amplified, the chopping frequency being preferably in excess of 100 cycles/sec for a tube amplifier, and in excess of 1000 cycles/sec for a transistor amplifier.

2. The expressions for mean-square noise voltage or current all contain a factor Δf; therefore the best noise figure will be obtained if the amplifier bandwidth is made as narrow as possible.

3. If the signal-to-noise ratio in the input signal is less than unity, the phase of the signal which is passed by a narrow-band amplifier will be governed mainly by the phase of the noise. In these circumstances the signal will tend to be lost, and the expected improvement in S/N caused by reducing Δf will not be obtained. (This is a manifestation of what is termed the "improvement threshold," i.e., once the condition of a signal has deteriorated beyond a certain point it becomes much more difficult to retrieve the desired information.) In this situation the signal and noise can often be separated: (a) by adding to the input signal a fixed, small amount of another signal which is *known* to be of the same phase as the signal it is desired to measure, so that the phase of the signal that is passed by the narrow-band amplifier will not be governed by the phase of the noise, and (b) by using a phase-sensitive detector to minimize noise in the rectified signal, as described in Chapter 6.

4. If a small input signal is superimposed on a large background signal, fluctuations in the background will be responsible for a disproportionate amount of the input noise. Therefore, for example, in radioactivity measurements the background count should be reduced as much as possible by paying particular attention to cleanliness, by careful shielding against external sources of high-energy radiation, and by the use of pulse-height discrimination. With photomultipliers at low light levels the main source of noise is

shot noise in the thermionic dark current. In critical applications the dark current is therefore reduced by cooling the tube with liquid nitrogen or solid CO_2. (In order to do this the whole tube is contained in a specially designed Dewar flask so as to prevent condensation on the window and make it less likely that the tube will suffer a fatal thermal shock.) An important advance here is the recent development of photomultipliers in which the effective area of the photocathode can be varied to suit the cross section of the incident light beam.[2] This confers the advantage that the dark current from a part of the photocathode which is not in use does not add its noise to the signal.

5. Noise is essentially statistical, and therefore over a long enough period can be expected to average out to zero. Expressed another way, the conclusion is that the greater the number of observations that are averaged, the greater the precision of the final result. This is particularly obvious in measurements of radioactivity, since the number of counts observed in unit time normally obeys a Poisson distribution, which is such that the standard deviation of any observation is *equal* to the square root of the number of counts in the observation. Electronically a signal can be averaged over a long period by using an output device with a slow response, for example, a meter with a long time constant. The only limitation here is set by the patience of the experimenter and the rate of change of the phenomenon which is being observed.

EXERCISES

8.1 Work out the value of f_2 for the 6AB4 grounded-grid amplifier of section 4d, assuming that stray capacitances in the output amount to 6 pF. Compare the answer with other results already obtained in section 8b.

8.2 Using equations (8.17) and (8.19), show that for a pentode the product of the mid-band gain and the value of f_2 (which is essentially equal to the bandwidth) in the grounded-cathode configuration is a characteristic of the tube itself when stray wiring capacitances can be neglected. Look up values of g_m and interelectrode capacitances for

---

[2] For example, ITT type FW118, manufactured by ITT Industrial Laboratories, Fort Wayne, Ind.

several different pentodes in tube manuals, and compare the merits of the tubes as amplifiers of high-frequency signals on this basis.

8.3 Suggest a means by which a capacitor of 100 μF and at least 350 V rating could be made to behave as a capacitance of 10,000 μF and approximately 3 V rating.

8.4 For the common-emitter stage of section 4c, assuming a collector-to-base capacitance of 2 pF, wiring capacitances in the output totaling 5 pF, and an input impedance of 2 K for the following stage, calculate the value of f_2 on the assumption that the α-cutoff frequency is very large. How large *would* f_α need to be in this case, in order for stray capacitance to be the limiting factor, if the mid-band value of β is 65?

8.5 A transducer has an output impedance of 100 ohms, and the only noise in the output signal is the Johnson noise appropriate to this value of resistance. Calculate the improvement in signal-to-noise ratio that would be obtained by using a step-up transformer to increase the signal voltage to the point at which the thermal noise was equal to the shot noise at the input to a 6AU6 amplifier (instead of simply taking the signal directly from the transducer to the grid). How is this result affected by the presence of other noise in the signal from the transducer? Make a general statement of the principle that is involved here.

REFERENCES

1. W. R. Bennett, *Electrical noise*. New York: McGraw-Hill Book Company, 1960.
2. A. Van der Ziel, *Noise*. Englewood Cliffs, N.J.: Prentice-Hall, 1954.
3. E. J. Bair, *Introduction to chemical instrumentation*. New York: McGraw-Hill Book Company, 1962, Chapter 7.
4. H. V. Malmstadt, C. G. Enke, and E. C. Toren, Jr., *Electronics for scientists*. New York: W. A. Benjamin, 1963, Chapter 4.
5. L. B. Arguimbau, *Vacuum-tube circuits and transistors*. New York: John Wiley & Sons, Inc., 1956, Chapters 3 and 15.

9

Oscillators and
Switching Circuits

....

9a INTRODUCTION

In Chapter 7 it was shown that the gain of an amplifier with
feedback is given by the expression

$$A' = A/(1 - A\phi) \tag{9.1}$$

where A is the open-loop gain of the amplifier and ϕ is the fraction of
the output that is fed back to the input. When the product $A\phi$ is
negative (the case of negative or *degenerative* feedback), it follows
that the gain A' is less than A and is effectively stabilized against
variations in the open-loop gain. Several of the applications of this
type of feedback were discussed in Chapter 7.

If $A\phi$ is positive the feedback is positive, or *regenerative*, and with
$A\phi$ between 0 and 1 the gain A' is greater than A and the circuit is
correspondingly unstable. If, in this case, the fraction ϕ is allowed
to increase slowly from zero, then at $A\phi = 1$ the circuit becomes so
unstable that any random fluctuation at the input is amplified and
fed back in such a way that a continuous oscillation results. Usually
the condition for oscillation is initially fulfilled at only one frequency,
so that the output from the circuit is in the form of a relatively pure
sine wave. Some oscillators which are designed to give this sort of
output will be described in section 9b. If ϕ is allowed to increase
still further, the voltage or current swings in the circuit grow to the
point at which they are limited by some circuit element overloading,

for example, a tube that is driven into the grid current region or cutoff. In this situation the output of the circuit is distorted, both because the tubes or transistors are operating in their nonlinear regions and because the condition $A\phi = 1$ is fulfilled at several frequencies simultaneously. In the limit the output signal is approximately a square wave, the tubes or transistors in the circuit being switched rapidly backwards and forwards between saturation and cutoff, and the circuit is then said to function as a *multivibrator*. By suitably adjusting the configurations of the active elements in a multivibrator, it is possible to arrange for either, both, or neither of the ON/OFF states to be stable, in which case the circuit is termed, respectively, a monostable, a bistable, or an astable multivibrator. These circuits are also called "trigger circuits," because they can be switched from one state to another, or out of a stable state and back again, by an external signal. They have found wide application in waveform and pulse generators, in nuclear pulse counters, and in electronic computers.

An alternative approach to switching circuits and waveform generators in general is by way of the *relaxation oscillator*; a simple example of this oscillator is given in Fig. 9.1. In this circuit the resistor R is chosen so that it cannot pass sufficient current to allow the glow tube to burn continuously when the voltage at A is equal to the burning voltage. As a result, if the tube is lit it goes out almost immediately, after which the capacitor C charges through R until the striking voltage is reached. At this point the glow tube ignites once more and rapidly discharges the capacitor, and the whole process is

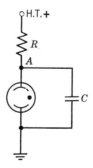

Fig. 9.1 Relaxation oscillator.

repeated.   Relaxation oscillators and trigger circuits will be discussed in some detail in section 9c.

9b   SINE-WAVE OSCILLATORS

In order to ensure that a circuit will oscillate at a single, predetermined frequency, it is usually necessary to include some sort of frequency-dependent network in the feedback loop.   At low frequencies this will take the form of a selective *RC* network, and at high frequencies it will normally be a tuned circuit.   A typical

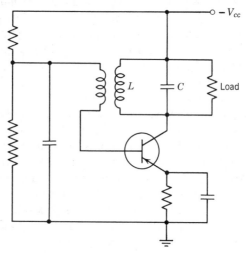

Fig. 9.2   Radio-frequency oscillator.

circuit for a transistor radio-frequency oscillator is illustrated in Fig. 9.2.   Here the positive feedback occurs through an rf transformer whose primary is one element of the tuned circuit.   The Q of the tuned circuit is somewhat reduced by the loading which results from energy dissipation in the base resistance of the transistor, since this resistance forms part of the circuit of the transformer secondary. The number of turns in the secondary is adjusted so that oscillation is just maintained.   The emitter resistor may be left unbypassed in order to introduce some negative feedback and so reduce the open-loop gain; alternatively, the open-loop gain can be adjusted to the point at which oscillation occurs by varying the fraction of the emitter resistor which is left unbypassed, as in Fig. 9.3.

A vast collection of high-frequency oscillator circuits is available in the literature, especially in the technical literature which is put out by the electronics industry. The selection of circuit configurations illustrated in Fig. 9.4 includes one in which the frequency is stabilized by means of a piezoelectric quartz crystal and another based on a tunnel diode. Fuller details and design procedures may be found in the references given at the end of this chapter.

Two possible circuit arrangements for an audio-frequency oscillator

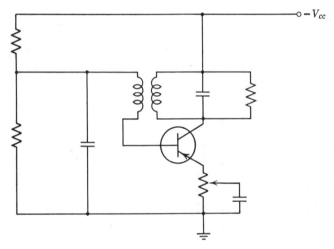

Fig. 9.3 Addition of amplitude control to Fig. 9.2.

based on a selective *RC* network are shown in block form in Fig. 9.5. If a network which produces a phase shift of 180° at the desired frequency is used, the oscillator can be constructed with only one tube or transistor, because of the 180° phase shift which is already present in the output from a common-cathode or common-emitter stage. If, however, the amplifier contains an even number of stages, a feedback network with zero phase shift at one particular frequency can cause it to oscillate at this frequency, provided the loop gain is sufficiently large.

A phase shift of 180° can be produced by either of the ladder

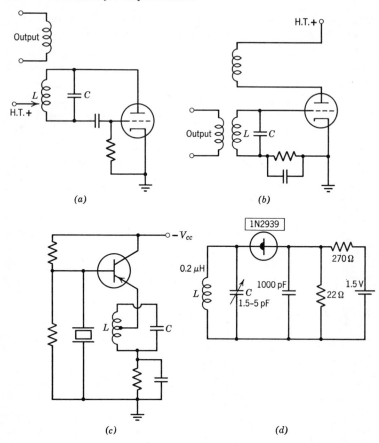

Fig. 9.4   Radio-frequency oscillators: (*a*) series-fed Hartley oscillator, (*b*) tuned grid oscillator, (*c*) crystal-controlled common-emitter oscillator, (*d*) 100 Mc tunnel diode negative-resistance oscillator (from *GE Tunnel Diode Manual*).

networks of Fig. 9.6, the frequency at which the 180° phase shift occurs being given by the expression

$$f = 1/2\pi RC\sqrt{6} \qquad\qquad (9.2)$$

At least three sections are required to produce the necessary phase shift, and it can be shown that the input voltage or current, depending

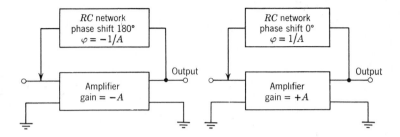

Fig. 9.5 *RC* oscillators.

on which is being fed back, is attenuated by a factor of 1/29. For zero phase shift it is possible to use the ladder network of Fig. 9.7a, for which the voltage attenuation at the frequency of zero phase shift was found in Exercise 1.3 to be one-third. The alternative is to use a Wien bridge network (Fig. 9.7b) for which the current attenuation, with output short-circuited, is one-third (cf. Exercise 9.1). For both of these networks the frequency of zero phase shift is given by the equation

$$f = 1/2\pi RC \qquad (9.3)$$

Two oscillator circuits which employ ladder networks with 180° phase shift are shown in Fig. 9.8, and two which employ networks with zero phase shift are shown in Fig. 9.9. In each circuit an adjustment is provided to enable either ϕ or the amplifier gain to be increased to the point at which oscillation is maintained and to control the amplitude of the output signals. With the transistor

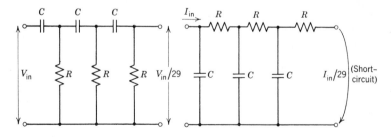

Fig. 9.6 Ladder networks for 180° phase shift.

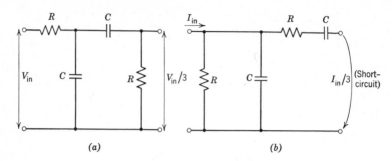

Fig. 9.7 Networks for zero phase shift.

circuits the output frequency is generally somewhat lower than would be expected from the formulas (9.2) and (9.3) because of the finite input and output impedances of the transistors. The phase-shift resistors are preferably chosen to be about halfway between the transistor input and output impedances, i.e., about 10 K, in order to minimize this effect.

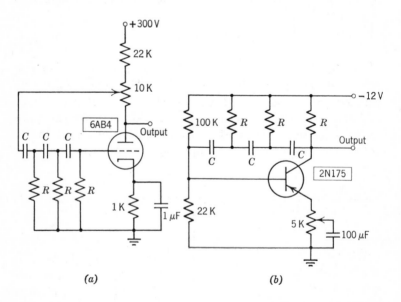

Fig. 9.8 180° phase-shift oscillators: $f = 1/2\pi RC\sqrt{6}$, (*a*) $R > 30$ K, (*b*) $R = 10$ K.

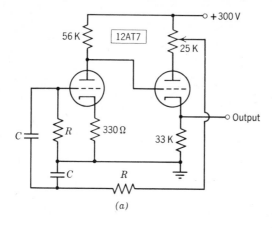

(a)

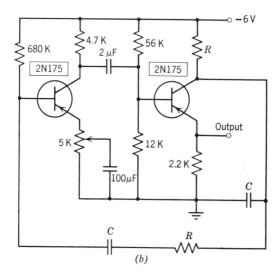

(b)

Fig. 9.9   Zero-phase-shift oscillators: (a) $R \geqslant 25$ K,
$f = 1/2\pi RC$, (b) $R = 10$ K, $f = 1/2\pi RC$.

If we wish to produce an extremely pure sine-wave oscillation in
the audio-frequency range, it appears that the best procedure is to
base the oscillator on a selective amplifier, such as one of those
described in Chapter 7.   The incorporation of a twin-T, negative-
feedback loop serves to reduce the gain at other than the chosen

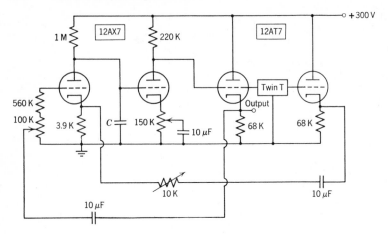

Fig. 9.10   Oscillator for producing a very pure sine-wave output.

frequency, and a nonselective, positive-feedback loop then brings
about the required oscillation.   A typical circuit is shown in Fig.
9.10.   As before, the small capacitor *C*, of about 330 pF, is inserted
if there is a tendency for unwanted oscillation to occur at high
frequencies.

9c   RELAXATION OSCILLATORS AND TRIGGER CIRCUITS

Saw-tooth Generators.   The output waveform from the relaxation
oscillator of Fig. 9.1 is illustrated in Fig. 9.11*a*.   In this figure the

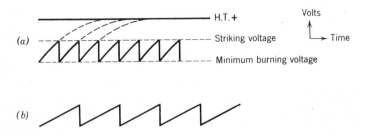

Fig. 9.11   (*a*) Waveforms for relaxation oscillator of Fig. 9.1, (*b*) ideal saw-
tooth waveform.

dotted curves show how the voltage on the capacitor would rise to the supply voltage level, with time constant RC, if the neon glow tube were not to halt the process when its striking voltage had been reached. The voltage falls rapidly once the glow tube has ignited, because the effective resistance of the tube is much less than R. The resulting output signal is quite a good approximation to a saw-tooth waveform, an ideal example of which is shown in Fig. 9.11b. This type of relaxation oscillator constitutes a particularly simple and inexpensive timing circuit, in which the repetition period can be varied over the range from minutes to milliseconds.

Generators of saw-tooth waveforms have many applications, the most important being that of driving the *time base* in an oscilloscope. In an oscilloscope a pattern is produced on a phosphorescent screen as a result of the combined vertical and horizontal deflection of an electron beam, which is focused to produce a bright spot on the screen. The vertical deflection of the beam is controlled by the voltage difference between a pair of plates, which are known as the "Y plates," and the horizontal deflection is similarly controlled by the voltage difference between a pair of "X plates" (Fig. 9.12). Usually the signal which is to be displayed is applied to the Y plates, and a time-base signal, i.e., a saw-tooth waveform, is applied to the X plates. The saw-tooth signal causes the electron beam to sweep steadily across the screen from left to right and then to fly back very quickly to the left-hand side before beginning another sweep. It is not too difficult to arrange for the time base to be synchronized with a repetitive signal which is applied to the Y plates, and the result is a

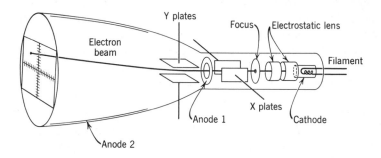

Fig. 9.12 Oscilloscope tube.

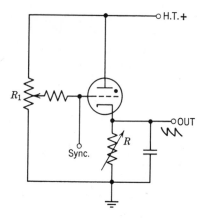

Fig. 9.13   Simple thyratron time base.

stationary display on the screen.   To prevent confusion which might result from the trace of the spot as it returns to the left of the screen, the electron gun is normally turned off by a "blanking pulse" during the flyback part of the cycle.

To illustrate the principle of operation of an oscilloscope time base we consider the thyratron relaxation oscillator of Fig. 9.13.   In this circuit if the thyratron is turned off the capacitor C discharges through R until the cathode potential has fallen sufficiently below the grid potential for the thyratron to fire.   The voltage at which firing occurs is governed by the setting of R_1.   When the thyratron fires the capacitor charges very rapidly to the supply voltage, after which the thyratron turns off again and the whole process is repeated. The output voltage falls exponentially when C is discharging, so if a very linear sweep is required it is necessary to connect R to a negative voltage supply, rather than to earth, or else to replace R by a constant-current tube, as in Fig. 9.14.   In Fig. 9.14 the current through R is governed by the setting of R_2, since the grid and cathode potentials of the pentode are practically equal when plate current is flowing. An alternative form of thyratron time base, in which the capacitor C ($= C_1 + C_2$) discharges through the thyratron and the saw-tooth output appears at the anode, is given in Fig. 9.15, where typical component values are specified.   With this arrangement the sharp rise in cathode potential that occurs when the thyratron fires is

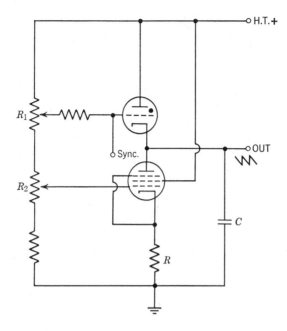

Fig. 9.14 Linear thyratron time base.

available in the form of a pulse which could serve as a blanking pulse if required. Thyratron time bases are limited to sweep frequencies below about 10 kc/sec because an appreciable time, known as the "deionization time," is required for ions to recombine with electrons in the tube after it has been switched off.

The usual method of synchronizing a time base with an incoming signal can also be illustrated with reference to these circuits. Here the signal is applied to the grid of the thyratron, through the connection labeled "sync." in the circuit diagrams, and it has the effect of reducing or increasing the repetition period of the saw-tooth waveform until it is equal to the period of the synchronizing signal. Let us consider the basic circuit of Fig. 9.13 and assume for simplicity that the thyratron fires when the grid and cathode voltages are exactly equal. Now if the falling portion of the saw-tooth waveform intercepts a rising portion of the input signal, as at A in Fig. 9.16a, and the natural period of the saw-tooth is longer than that of

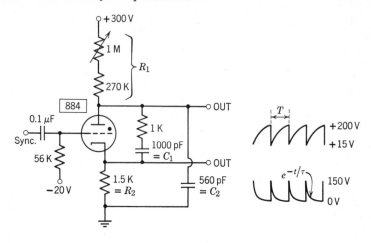

Fig. 9.15   Thyratron time base with pulse output: $T \sim R_1(C_1 + C_2)$, $\tau = R_2 C_2$.

the input signal, the period of the saw-tooth will be shortened because the next interception point will occur earlier in the period, as at *B* in Fig. 9.16*a*.   If the period of the saw-tooth is still too long, the subsequent interception will occur earlier still, as at *C* in Fig. 9.16*a*, and the shortening process will continue until the two signals are synchronized, provided the initial difference between the repetition periods is not too great.   Similarly, if the period of the saw-tooth is initially a little too short, the interception point will tend to move down the rising portion of the input signal until synchronization is achieved.   If the period of the saw-tooth is much longer than that of the input signal, it can be synchronized with a submultiple of the input signal frequency, as in Fig. 9.16*b*.   This last observation will be familiar to anyone who has ever used an oscilloscope.

A great many time-base circuits have been designed and may be found in the literature and in the references listed at the end of this chapter.   Before leaving this topic, however, we shall consider one more circuit which is remarkable both for the linearity of its output and for the variety of its applications.   This is the *Miller time base*, an example of which is given in Fig. 9.17.   The tube used here is one with a very short suppressor base (cf. the gated amplifier of Chapter 6), but an ordinary pentode could be used as well, or even a

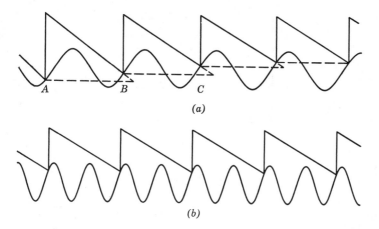

(a)

(b)

Fig. 9.16 (a) Synchronization of a time base, (b) synchronization of a time base with a submultiple of the input frequency.

triode with the gating signal applied to the control grid. The reader should verify that the tube ratings are not likely to be exceeded with the component values shown in Fig. 9.17. To explain the operation of this circuit we consider the simplified diagram of Fig. 9.18. Suppose that grid 3 of the tube is initially at − 10 V, so that the plate current is completely cut off. About 9 mA will flow through the 22 K resistor to grid 2, whose potential in these circumstances is found from the characteristics to be + 100 V. Grid current will also flow through R to grid 1 and this grid will be close to earth potential. If the plate current is now turned on suddenly as a result of a positive

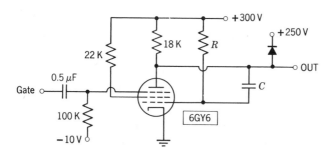

Fig. 9.17   Miller sweep circuit: $R \geqslant 100$ K.

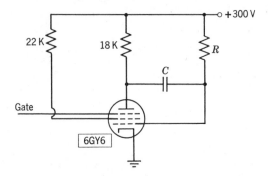

Fig. 9.18   Basis of Miller sweep circuit.

gate being applied to grid 3 (Fig. 9.19), the plate voltage begins to fall very rapidly.   This drop in plate voltage is transmitted to the control grid through the capacitor C and immediately causes the tube to be almost cut off.   Hence the initial fall in plate voltage amounts to only about 4.5 V, this being the size of the grid base. The plate voltage then begins to fall more steadily, after its initial rapid drop, while the grid voltage rises slowly as C is charged by the almost constant current through R.   (This current is almost constant because g_1 remains within 5 V of earth potential.)

If the amplification of the tube is A the grid potential changes by only V/A volts when the anode potential is swept through a voltage V. Because of the Miller effect the capacitor C appears, from the point of view of the control grid, to have a capacitance equal to $C(1 - A)$, where in the present example A is equal to -59, so that the grid

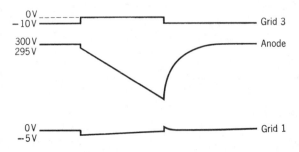

Fig. 9.19   Waveforms in Miller time base.

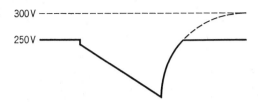

Fig. 9.20   Anode waveform with catching diode.

potential changes at a rate which is only $1/(1 - A) = 1/60$ of the rate at which it would change if the anode end of C were connected to earth. The corresponding change in anode potential is therefore $A/(1 - A)$ times the change in *grid potential* that would occur if the anode end of C were connected to earth, and this is virtually independent of the characteristics of the tube.   Here is the explanation of the extreme linearity of the output signal at the anode, and it follows that the slope of the waveform is given to a good approximation by the equation

$$\frac{dV}{dt} = \frac{-AV_o}{RC(1 - A)} \tag{9.4}$$

where V_o is the supply voltage.

When the gate is turned off the grid and plate potentials change rapidly by 2 or 3 V, as in Fig. 9.19, and the capacitor C charges to 300 V via the 18 K resistor.   Thus the slope of the linear portion of the waveform is governed by the magnitudes of R and C, and the final return to $+300$ V is governed by C and the anode load.   The "catching diode" of Fig. 9.17 has the effect of catching the anode at $+250$ V and so reducing the time required for flyback (Fig. 9.20). This method of obtaining a highly linear sweep voltage, i.e., by charging a capacitor with a constant current, is used in many timing circuits.

Square-Wave Generators: Schmitt Trigger.   The Schmitt trigger is a particularly simple and useful form of square-wave generator.   This circuit, for which tube and transistor examples are shown in Fig. 9.21, possesses two stable states which are such that the state that the circuit is in is governed by the dc voltage level at the input.   This property enables the Schmitt trigger to function as a voltage discriminator, and as a device for converting a signal of arbitrary form

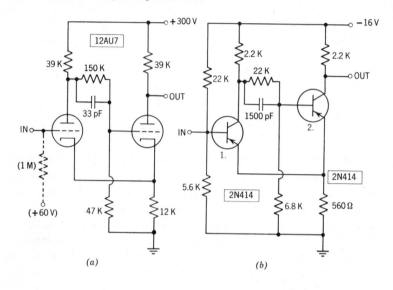

Fig. 9.21   Schmitt triggers.

into a square wave.   In the latter role it is often used to convert a
reference signal from a chopper into a standardized square wave for
gating a phase-sensitive detector (section 6c).   Another application
is as a generator of sharp pulses: in this application the usual square-
wave output is differentiated and the negative-going pulses are
eliminated by means of a series diode (cf. Fig. 6.20).   The operation
of a Schmitt trigger will be explained with reference to the transistor
circuit of Fig. 9.21b.   The explanation for the tube circuit of Fig.
9.21a is essentially the same and the details will be left as an exercise
for the reader (Exercise 9.2).

The circuit shown uses 2N414 transistors ($\beta = 80$, $f_\alpha = 8$ Mc,
i_c max $= 200$ mA), but the choice of transistor is not very critical.
Here the collector current is chosen to be 5 mA, and the biasing
resistors have been chosen so that in the absence of any external
influence this current normally flows through transistor 1.   Therefore the emitter potential, which is the same for both transistors, is
-2.8 V, and the potential of collector 1 is -5 V.   The potential
divider comprising the 22 K and 6.8 K resistors fixes the potential
of base 2 at -1.2 V, so transistor 2 is completely cut off.   The

output voltage from collector 2 is close to -16 V, since the collector leakage current under these conditions is only about 5 μA.

If an incoming signal causes the negative input voltage at base 1 to become less than about -3 V, the current through transistor 1 begins to decrease. The negative collector voltage therefore increases, towards -16 V, and this increase is transferred to the base of transistor 2 by way of the potential divider. Therefore the base voltage of transistor 2 increases at the same time that the mutual emitter voltage is decreasing because of transistor 1 being cut off, and the result is that transistor 2 is switched on very rapidly. This causes the emitter voltage to begin to increase again and so speeds the cutoff of transistor 1. As a result, a new stable state is reached, with transistor 1 completely cut off and with the output voltage at collector 2 close to -5 V. (If the collector load were chosen so that the transistor became "bottomed," or "saturated," this voltage would be close to -3 V.) If the input voltage at base 1 is now made more negative than about -3 V, transistor 1 begins to turn on and the whole process is repeated in reverse, so that the circuit switches back very rapidly to the original stable state. It follows that whatever the shape of the input signal, the output is a square wave of amplitude 11 V. The capacitor which is inserted between collector 1 and base 2 is intended to transmit the rapid change of collector potential directly to the base and so facilitate rapid switching, which is essential if the circuit is to produce a square wave with sharp corners. The capacitor, whose value is not critical, also helps to reduce the switching time in a transistor circuit by enabling the stored charge in the base region to be neutralized quickly. The optimum value for this capacitor depends on the frequency of operation, a larger value being required at low frequencies. The value specified here is suitable for frequencies of the order of 50 or 100 kc.

Because some current has to flow into or out of base 1, the output impedance of the signal source should not be too high for a Schmitt trigger using transistors, or the circuit is likely to be rather insensitive. If the circuit of Fig. 9.21 were to be driven from a source of moderately high impedance, say 10 K, it would be preferable to replace the 22 K and 5.6 K biasing resistors by a single 220 K resistor between base 1 and the -16 V supply.

In designing a Schmitt trigger the procedure is first to choose the supply voltage, which in the case of a transistor circuit should usually be at least 3 V greater than the amplitude of the desired square wave. Once the supply voltage is fixed a transistor can be chosen to have the necessary voltage rating and suitable high-frequency characteristics. The current through the ON transistor can then be fixed, and the emitter resistor can be chosen to give a suitable emitter potential, typically 2 to 6 V. The emitter potential governs the base potential of transistor 1, and hence the size of the biasing resistor or resistors. The sizes of the collector loads are fixed in accordance with the required amplitude of the output signal, and the resistors in the potential divider which takes the signal to the base of transistor 2 are calculated so that this transistor is definitely OFF when transistor 1 is conducting, and definitely ON when transistor 1 is OFF. The resistors in the potential divider should work out to be about an order of magnitude larger than the collector load of transistor 1. The capacitor in the potential divider can be chosen empirically to suit the frequency of operation.

A typical switching cycle, showing the variation of output voltage with input voltage, is illustrated in Fig. 9.22. Beginning with transistor 1 ON and the output at −16 V, the circuit switches to the other stable state when the input voltage becomes slightly more positive than −3 V. When transistor 1 is OFF, on the other hand, the input has to become slightly more negative than −3 V before

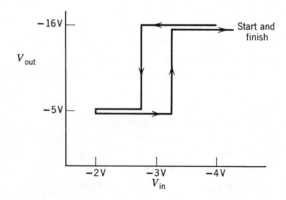

Fig. 9.22   Hysteresis in a Schmitt trigger.

triggering occurs. The difference between the critical voltages for switching in the two directions is termed "hysteresis." The magnitude of the difference is dependent on the gain around the regenerative loop: base 1 → collector 1 → base 2 → emitter 2 → emitter 1 → base 1. The greater the loop gain, the greater the hysteresis, which just disappears when the loop gain is equal to 1. For proper trigger action the loop gain must be greater than 1. If it is less than unity the Schmitt trigger degenerates into an amplifier with positive feedback, such that saturation occurs with very small signal voltages. In this case there are intermediate states, between ON and OFF, which are stable provided the input voltage remains constant. Once the loop gain exceeds 1 the intermediate states become unstable and the circuit must switch through any intermediate state into one of the stable states. The nature of the stable state into which it switches is then governed by the previous history of the circuit.

Square-Wave Generators: Multivibrators. Here we consider square-wave generators whose transition from one stable or metastable state to another is able to be initiated by an externally applied *pulse*. Basic circuits for astable, monostable, and bistable multivibrators are given in Fig. 9.23, and it is immediately apparent that the degree of stability of the states of a multivibrator is governed by the nature of the coupling in the regenerative loop between the two transistors. In general, ac coupling gives rise to metastable states and dc coupling gives rise to stable states. We shall consider the operation of each of these circuits in turn.

The astable (or free-running) multivibrator of Fig. 9.23a has a regenerative loop: base 1 → collector 1 → base 2 → collector 2 → base 1 which tends to exaggerate any imbalance in the currents through the two transistors. Therefore as soon as the circuit is switched on it enters a state in which one transistor is conducting and the other is cut off. In this state, if transistor 1 is ON, capacitor C_1 has one side (collector 1) held near earth potential, while the other side (base 2) has been driven positive with respect to earth potential by the switching transient from collector 1. Capacitor C_1 therefore charges through R_1 until the base potential of transistor 2 has risen to the point at which the transistor begins to conduct. Regenerative switching then takes place, and the circuit enters a new metastable state with transistor 1 OFF and transistor 2 ON, where it

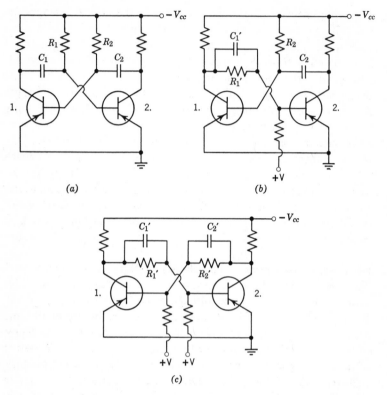

Fig. 9.23   Multivibrators; (*a*) astable, (*b*) monostable, (*c*) bistable.

remains until capacitor C_2 has charged through R_2.   If $R_1C_1 \neq R_2C_2$ the output square wave is unsymmetrical.   The duration of the metastable state is approximately $0.7R_1C_1$, or $0.7R_2C_2$, respectively. The circuit can be triggered, or synchronized, by means of pulse or sine-wave signals applied to either base in essentially the same manner that the thyratron oscillator of Fig. 9.13 was triggered.   By arranging that the circuit is triggered by, say, every fifth pulse applied to one of the bases, it can be made to function as a frequency divider.

Typical component values and waveforms for tube and transistor versions of this circuit are given in Figs. 9.24 and 9.25.   For variety, Fig. 9.25 uses *npn* transistors, so that the polarities of the circuit voltages are the reverse of those in Fig. 9.23.

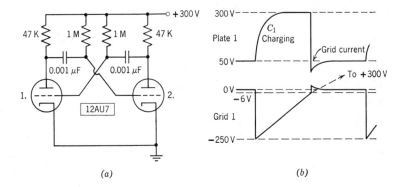

(a)   (b)

Fig. 9.24 Astable multivibrator using tubes: (a) typical circuit; (b) waveforms for tube 1. (Note that the 12AU7 is rated to withstand negative grid voltages down to −660 V in short pulses.)

The monostable multivibrator (or univibrator, one-shot multivibrator, or start-stop multivibrator) of Fig. 9.23b has the base potential of transistor 2 fixed so that this transistor is normally cut off in the quiescent state of the circuit.   If a negative current pulse is applied to base 2, or a positive pulse to base 1, regenerative switching occurs so that transistor 1 is turned OFF and transistor 2 is turned ON. Capacitor C_2 now charges through R_2 to the point at which transistor 1 turns ON again, thus cutting off transistor 2 and completing the cycle.   The function of the capacitor C_1' is the same as that of the

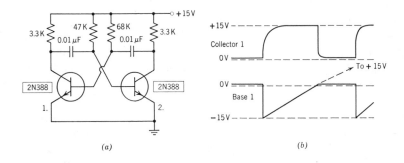

(a)   (b)

Fig. 9.25 Astable multivibrator using *npn* transistors: (a) typical circuit, (b) waveforms.

similar capacitor in the Schmitt trigger, i.e., it transfers the rapid voltage change from collector 1 to base 2 without attenuation. Typical circuits and waveforms are shown in Figs. 9.26 and 9.27. To avoid the necessity of having two power supplies the circuits which are given here are self-biased by way of a shared cathode or emitter resistor, as was the case with the Schmitt triggers of Fig. 9.21. Similar component values are used in these circuits in order to emphasize their relationship to the Schmitt triggers. The univibrator has the useful property of being able to be triggered, by pulses of various shapes and amplitudes, to give an output pulse of a standard size and shape, i.e., it can function as a *pulse shaper.* It can also be used as a pulse-delay circuit, if it is arranged that the subsequent circuit is triggered by a signal derived from the trailing edge of the univibrator output pulse.

The bistable multivibrator (or flip-flop, binary, or Eccles-Jordan trigger circuit) of Fig. 9.23c is an essential component of practically every piece of electronic equipment that has to deal with information in the form of discrete pulses. The simplest application is as a binary counter, or scale of 2, which makes use of the fact that two input pulses are required to produce one complete output pulse. Other applications include the production of gating signals, information storage (in the form of a binary digit, or "bit," of information), and the carrying out of the various arithmetic operations which are involved in high-speed computing. Typical transistor and tube examples of this circuit, with self-bias and using similar components to those in Fig. 9.21, are given in Figs. 9.28 and 9.29. The drawing of typical waveforms for these circuits is left as an exercise for the reader (Exercise 9.3).

A flip-flop can be triggered by a pulse applied at any point where it will initiate the regenerative switching cycle, for example, a negative pulse can be applied to the plate of an OFF tube, the grid of an ON tube, the collector of an ON transistor, or the base of an OFF transistor. If the available trigger pulses are of one sign only, it is necessary to ensure that the incoming pulses are steered to the place where they will produce the desired effect. This is usually accomplished with the aid of pulse-steering diodes, in the manner illustrated in Fig. 9.30. The diodes are chosen on the basis of their peak inverse voltage rating and switching speed, since they are not likely to be required to deliver an appreciable current.

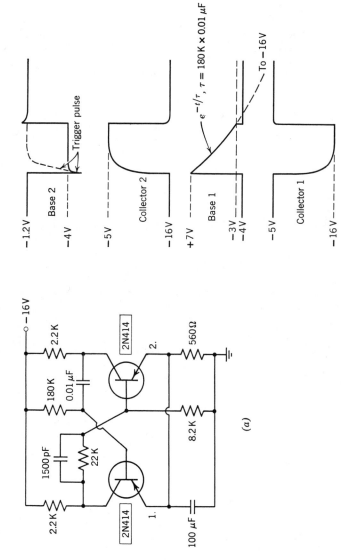

Fig. 9.26 Univibrator (cf. Fig. 9.21*b*): (*a*) typical circuit using transistors, (*b*) waveforms.

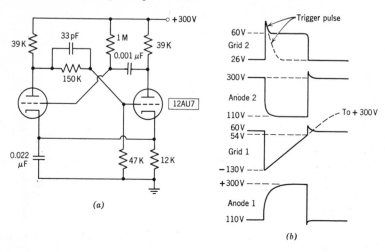

Fig. 9.27   Univibrator (cf. Fig. 9.21a): (a) typical circuit using tubes, (b) wave-forms.

Frequency Limitations of Pulse Circuits.   The term "pulse circuits" covers pulse amplifiers in addition to the switching circuits that we have considered so far in this section.   The main task of a pulse

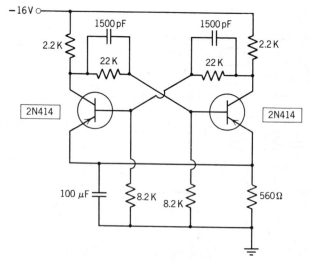

Fig. 9.28   Bistable multivibrator using transistors.

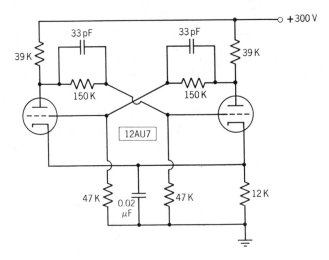

Fig. 9.29 Bistable multivibrator using tubes.

amplifier is to transmit sharp-edged pulses and increase their amplitude with as little distortion as possible. With switching circuits, i.e., pulse generators, on the other hand, the aim is to bring about successive, rapid transitions between saturation and cutoff. The main consideration with pulse amplifiers, at least with small pulses, is the amplifier bandwidth, but with switching circuits it is the magnitudes of the rise and fall times for the process of switching a tube or transistor on and off.

If a square pulse is fed into a circuit with a limited high-frequency response (a "low-pass" circuit), the effect on the pulse is similar to the action of the integrating network which was described in Chapter 1, i.e., a very short pulse fails to attain its full amplitude, and in the limit appears as a voltage step (Figs. 9.31*a* and 9.31*b*). Therefore, in order to amplify small pulses faithfully, it is necessary for the bandwidth of the amplifier to be greater than the reciprocal of the pulse length, and this leads to the problems associated with the design of very wide band amplifiers, as discussed in Chapter 8. The bandwidth is a good indication of the ability of an amplifier to handle small pulses with a minimum of distortion, but with very large pulses it is obvious that, for example, an amplifier whose output stage can deliver at most 10 mA when turned full on will not be able

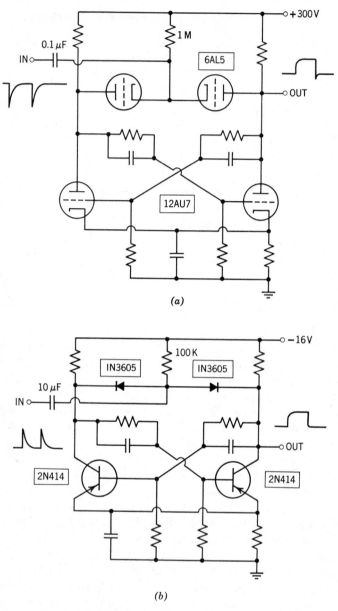

Fig. 9.30 Use of pulse-steering diodes: (a) negative pulse steered to anode of OFF tube, (b) positive pulse steered to collector of OFF transistor.

to deliver a 100 V pulse into a capacitive load of 100 pF, i.e., a charge of 10^{-8} coulomb, in less than a microsecond, whatever the bandwidth may be for small signals.

Normally a pulse amplifier does not need to possess a particularly good low-frequency response; however, if the low-frequency response is very limited the effect on a long input pulse is equivalent to the effect of the differentiating network of Chapter 1 (Fig. 9.31c). Short pulses are transmitted more or less faithfully, but the tops of long pulses have a marked slope, or "tilt," and the end of a positive pulse is followed by a negative excursion before the output voltage returns to the level of the base line. Each succeeding stage with limited low-frequency response adds one more positive or negative voltage excursion after the pulse proper, the effect of three stages

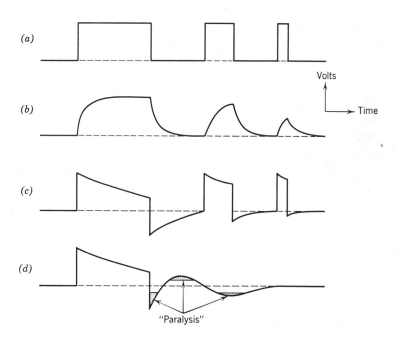

Fig. 9.31 Bandwidth limitations in a pulse amplifier: (a) input pulses, (b) output with inadequate high-frequency response, (c) output with inadequate low-frequency response, (d) output from three stages with inadequate low-frequency response, for a single input pulse.

being shown in Fig. 9.31c. With large pulses these unwanted excursions may be sufficient to produce *paralysis* or *blocking*, i.e., a following stage can be overloaded and so put out of action for some time after the initial pulse has gone by (shaded areas in Fig. 9.31c). For a satisfactorily flat base line, with negligible paralysis, the coupling time constants of the amplifier stages must be much greater than the duration of the pulses.

The *rise time* and *fall time* of a switching circuit are defined respectively as the time required for the output signal to swing between 10 and 90% of its maximum value on the way up, and between 90 and 10% of its maximum value on the way down. The *delay time* is the time for the first 10% of the change to occur on the way up, and the *storage time* is the time for the first 10% of the change to occur on the way down. These last two definitions are of particular significance with regard to transistor switching, in which the rate of diffusion of holes in the base region is an important limitation. With tubes the main delaying factors are the times required to charge and discharge stray capacitances. These effects were considered in essence in Chapter 8 and will not be dealt with here.

A full account of the factors which govern the transient response characteristics of switching transistors is given in the *GE Transistor Manual* (reference 5 in the list at the end of this chapter). In what follows we shall summarize the main points of this discussion.

Consider the circuit of Fig. 9.32. If the switch S is opened and

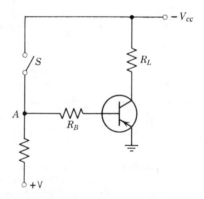

Fig. 9.32   Basic switching circuit.

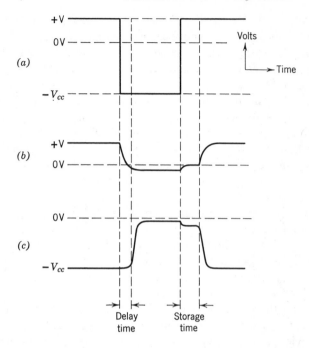

Fig. 9.33 Transistor switching waveforms: (a) voltage at
A; (b) voltage at base; (c) voltage at collector.

closed very rapidly, the resulting input waveform at A is as shown in
Fig. 9.33a. The corresponding base voltage (Fig. 9.33b) falls fairly
quickly to slightly below earth potential and begins the process of
switching the collector current on. This process is delayed (Fig.
9.33c) because of the time required for the base current to charge the
depletion-layer capacitances at the collector and emitter junctions,
for the emitter current to diffuse across the base, and for the current
gain and frequency response to increase from the low values which
they have at low current densities. The collector voltage is shown
in Fig. 9.33c as rising almost to earth potential, corresponding to
saturation of the transistor with both collector and emitter junctions
forward-biased. As a result of this saturation some charge is stored
in the base region, and when the switch is opened again the transistor
cannot turn off until this stored charge has diffused away into the

collector.   Therefore, when the switch is opened, the base voltage cannot immediately rise above earth potential because the transistor is still conducting.   Once the stored charge has diffused or been swept away, the collector and base voltages return to their initial values.

Typically, for a *pnp* alloy transistor type 2N396 ($f_\alpha = 5$ Mc) the delay time is about 0.1 or 0.2 μsec, the rise time is 0.1 to 0.5 μsec, the storage time is 0.2 to 1.0 μsec, and the fall time is about 0.2 μsec, where the actual values vary markedly with the operating conditions. The magnitudes of these effects depend on the load impedance (through which the stored charge must flow), the current gain required from the transistor, the size of the current which can be delivered to the base through the resistance R_B, the thickness of the base layer (reflected in the value of f_α), and the biasing conditions before closing the switch (which govern the amount of charging or discharging of capacitances that is required).   Various techniques have been devised for reducing these effects—for example, the use of a diode clamp to prevent the collector voltage falling to the saturation value and the use of a capacitor in parallel with R_B to neutralize stored charge in the base region, as has already been mentioned in connection with the Schmitt trigger.   If saturation *is* permitted to occur, it confers the advantage that the output voltage is relatively independent of the properties of the individual transistor in the circuit.   For further details the reader is referred to the literature and, in particular, to the *GE Transistor Manual*.

EXERCISES

9.1   Calculate the values of the attenuation factors for the current and voltage networks shown in the accompanying figure, at the frequency of the indicated phase shift in each case.   Comment on the results.

9.2   Estimate the size of the output signal from the Schmitt trigger of Fig. 9.21*a*.   Sketch typical waveforms for both of the circuits in Fig. 9.21.

9.3   Sketch the waveforms which you would expect to observe for the bistable multivibrators of Fig. 9.30.

9.4   Begin by designing a long-tailed pair circuit based on either a 12AU7 double triode or two 2N414 switching transistors.   Modify the circuit appropriately so as to convert it into (a) a Schmitt trigger, (b) a bistable

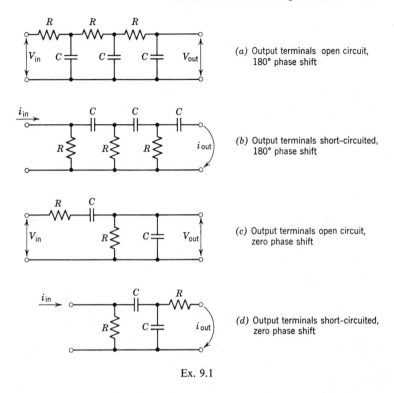

(a) Output terminals open circuit, 180° phase shift

(b) Output terminals short-circuited, 180° phase shift

(c) Output terminals open circuit, zero phase shift

(d) Output terminals short-circuited, zero phase shift

Ex. 9.1

multivibrator, (c) a monostable multivibrator, (d) a univibrator, (e) a sinusoidal oscillator with a selective RC feedback network.

REFERENCES

1. F. J. M. Farley, *Elements of pulse circuits*. London: Methuen & Co., 1955.
2. W. C. Elmore and M. Sands, *Electronics*. New York: McGraw-Hill Book Company, 1949.
3. H. V. Malmstadt, C. G. Enke, and E. C. Toren, Jr., *Electronics for scientists*. New York: W. A. Benjamin, 1963, Chapters 5 and 9.
4. E. J. Bair, *Introduction to chemical instrumentation*. New York: McGraw-Hill Book Company, 1962, Chapters 4 and 5.
5. *GE transistor manual*. Syracuse, N.Y.: General Electric Company, Sixth Edition, 1962, Chapter 6.
6. *Mullard reference manual of transistor circuits*. London: Mullard, Ltd., 1960, Chapters 23 and 24.

10

Electronic Instrumentation

....

10a INTRODUCTION

Once a certain amount of basic understanding has been gained, electronics becomes almost entirely a practical art. Thus it is normally much more important to be able to design and build a usable piece of equipment than to be able to produce a high-powered mathematical explanation of how it works. This should be especially true for the readers of this book, whose usual procedure will probably be first to design a circuit on the basis of more or less approximate calculations, and then to determine its precise performance by experiment, followed if necessary by modification or trouble-shooting. Certainly this is the author's own approach. It follows that no book on electronics is complete without some indication of how the circuit diagrams, which have usually been discussed at some length, may be converted into functioning hardware. Without some such discussion the subject is likely to degenerate into an abstract pastime, almost a branch of topology.

This final chapter is intended to provide an introduction to the practical side of electronics, notably to circuit building and testing procedures, the functions of test instruments, and trouble-shooting. In this connection the practical sections of the references listed at the end of the chapter should also be helpful. Reference 1 (Malmstadt, Enke, and Toren: *Electronics for Scientists*) is particularly outstanding in this regard. One other topic of a practical nature concerns the question of how a number of different circuits can be combined together so as to make up a complete instrument. The answer to this question will take the form of a description of several practical instruments which are based mainly upon circuits that have been described so far in this book.   Several of these instruments have been very useful in the past, and it may be that the reader will find some applications for the circuits in his own experimental work.

10b   CIRCUIT BUILDING, TESTING, AND TROUBLE-SHOOTING

Circuit Building.   The builder of a piece of electronic equipment usually has quite a small number of definite objectives, and the variety of ways in which these can be attained is limited only by human ingenuity.   Nevertheless, it is generally preferable to fix on one or two of the many possible systems of construction in order to achieve simplicity and uniformity in large pieces of equipment, and to make it possible to move an instrument from one project to another with a minimum of fuss.   Therefore with "building block" units, such as power supplies, amplifiers, pulse counters, etc., it is recommended that electronic equipment be constructed to fit into the 19-inch rack-and-panel system illustrated in Fig. 10.1.   Within this system it is possible to achieve a good deal of variety by having different arrangements of chassis and subchassis mounted vertically or horizontally behind the front panel.   Switches, meters, and controls are mounted on the front panel and connecting cables are

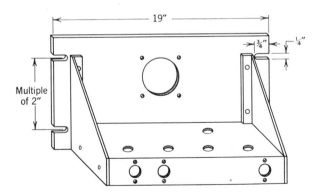

Fig. 10.1   Chassis for 19-inch rack-and-panel system.

attached at the rear.   A variant of this arrangement has each panel with its attached chassis able to be slid out from the rack like a drawer in a filing cabinet, so that an instrument can be serviced from the front, with consequent economy in laboratory space.   The only restriction in practice is that heavy components such as transformers and chokes need to be mounted close to the supporting rack.   For small, self-contained units, on the other hand, the rack-and-panel system has no special advantage, and a method of construction such as that illustrated in Fig. 10.2 for a photometer with integral power supplies is commonly adopted.

The aims of a circuit builder are, apart from the obvious one of providing mechanical support for the components, to produce a finished product which is reasonably compact, in which heat generated in the components can be dissipated safely, in which unwanted interactions cannot occur between different parts of the circuit, in which it is easy to introduce a probe at different parts of the circuit in order to test its performance, and in which it is easy to remove one component and substitute another during trouble-shooting.   To see how these aims are commonly achieved in practice, we shall consider three typical examples, namely, the tuned audio-frequency amplifier of Fig. 7.13; a wide-band, low-noise amplifier with the first stage a cascode amplifier similar to Fig. 5.5

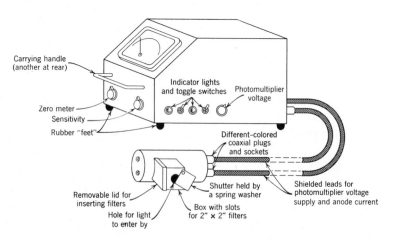

Fig. 10.2   Mode of construction for a portable photometer.

and several subsequent stages similar to the pentode amplifier of Fig. 4.8 (all with greatly reduced anode load, say 2.2 K); and the transistorized power supply of Fig. 7.17.

The layout of the audio-frequency amplifier at the stage just before wiring the components together is illustrated in Fig. 10.3. At audio frequencies it is not difficult to avoid interactions between one part of a circuit and another, provided only that grid leads are kept as short as possible. Resistor mounting strips ("tag strips") are convenient to use in this case, and with them it is very easy to make point checks of voltages and waveforms at different parts of the circuit. The resistors and other small components are, naturally, mounted as close as possible to the components and the tube socket to which they are to be connected. Components which are too large for the mounting strips, such as large electrolytic capacitors, are held in spring clips (e.g., "Terry" clips) bolted to the chassis. The

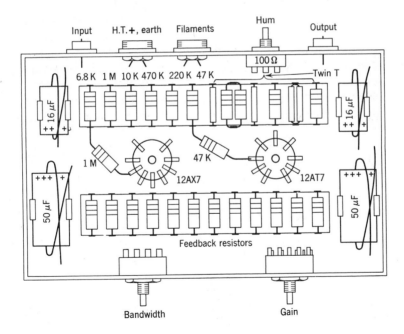

Fig. 10.3   Layout of an audio-frequency amplifier (to occupy half of a 19-inch panel). Cf. Fig. 7.13.

metal screens at the centers of tube sockets are connected to the earth line, which is firmly attached to the chassis at a single point. The input and output signals enter and leave via coaxial sockets, and the ac filament supply, +300 V, and earth connections enter through a suitable multipin plug or plugs. For this particular circuit two multiposition rotary switches are required on the front panel, one to control the gain and the other the bandwidth of the amplifier. The various feedback resistors are therefore mounted on the panel side of the chassis. In wiring a circuit of this type it is generally preferable to use single-strand, tinned copper wire of about 22 gauge, with lengths of different-colored sleeving to label the connections as filament leads, +300 V, earth, grid, cathode, feedback loops, etc. Because the wire is moderately stiff it can be pulled straight or given several right-angle bends and be expected to remain that way, so that the chance of producing a bird's nest is minimized. The different stages of making a reliable soldered connection are illustrated in Fig. 10.4. The first wires to be soldered in are the filament leads, which should be twisted together in order to reduce the transmission of hum to the rest of the circuit. It is usual to earth the side of the filament for which the leads are least shielded from the rest of the circuit; an alternative and often superior procedure is to insert a 100 ohm potentiometer between the two leads and attach the sliding contact of the potentiometer to earth. The potentiometer setting is then adjusted empirically so as to minimize the amount of mains hum in the output.

The manner in which the style of amplifier construction is varied to suit a wide-band amplifier is shown in Fig. 10.5. The main point in this case is to keep all signal-carrying leads, and especially grid leads, as short as possible. With this in mind the tube sockets are mounted close to one another (the tubes themselves are invariably shielded with metal cans) and are oriented so that signals pass in a direct line from the anode of one tube to the grid of the next. This linear arrangement also reduces the likelihood of unpleasant interactions between one end of the amplifier and the other. The 300 V and earth lines are made in the form of "bus bars," i.e., heavy, uninsulated, tinned copper wire, typically gauge 14 or 16, stretched between short, insulated posts at opposite ends of the line of tubes. Feedback resistors, if they are introduced, are firmly mounted on tag strips, as in the audio-frequency amplifier. Feedback will normally

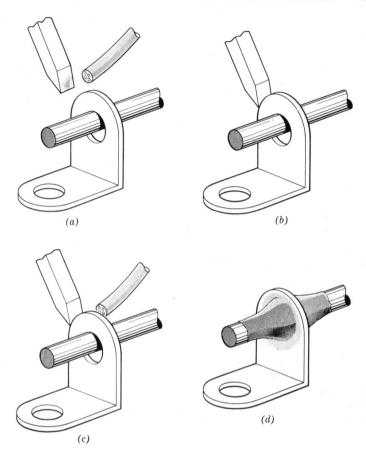

Fig. 10.4 Steps in making a soldered joint: (*a*) tip of soldering iron tinned lightly, (*b*) heat applied to parts to be soldered, (*c*) solder (with flux in cores) applied to hot metal, (*d*) heat removed and joint allowed to cool without parts moving.

be taken over one or two stages only, and successive feedback loops can usefully be placed on opposite sides of the chassis, as in Fig. 10.5. For shielding purposes the components are normally mounted very close to the chassis, so it may be necessary to drill holes here and there in order to help ventilate resistors which are dissipating more than 1 or 2 W.

The transistorized power supply of Fig. 7.17 is an example of a circuit in which the main consideration is getting rid of heat. The problem is simplified by the fact that the components (Fig. 10.6) are constructed to facilitate mounting on heat sinks. Here the whole circuit could be built on a single earthed chassis, which would serve as a general heat sink, with thin (0.002-inch) mica washers and insulating bushes to isolate the anodes of the 1N612R rectifiers and

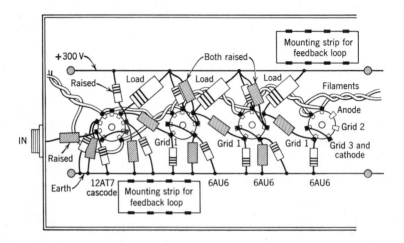

Fig. 10.5 Style of construction for a wide-band amplifier, e.g., a pulse amplifier. Capacitors shaded, resistors with color-coding rings indicated. Actual sizes (and shapes) of capacitors depend on performance required at low frequencies.

the collector of the 2N1905 transistor from earth potential. Alternatively, the 1N612R rectifiers and 2N1905 transistor could be mounted on a separate aluminium plate (about 4 × 4 inches) attached to the main chassis (say 6 × 4½ inches and 2 inches deep) by insulated posts, with other components hung in the space between them. Another method is to construct a chassis in the form of a box, two opposite sides of which are aluminium heat sinks; the other two are printed circuit board, or one of the many types of perforated circuit boards which are available for mounting the small components commonly used in transistor circuits. Sheet Perspex, Lucite, and Plexiglass are often convenient materials for constructing spacers to fit between heat sinks, both because they are transparent and because, owing to their thermoplastic nature, metal screws can make their own "tapped" holes if an undersize hole is drilled first and the screw is pushed home with a hot soldering iron. These materials are also useful in high-voltage circuits, such as the power supply of Fig. 7.20, and to a lesser extent in electrometer circuits, because of their excellent insulating properties.

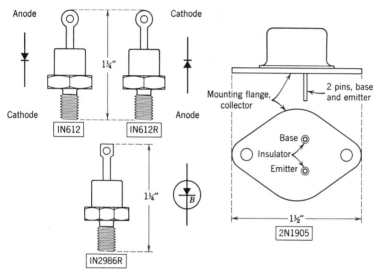

Fig. 10.6   Components designed to facilitate mounting on heat sinks.

Testing and Trouble-Shooting. The basic instruments which are required for testing and trouble-shooting are an oscilloscope, a signal generator, a multimeter, and a vacuum tube voltmeter. The operation of an oscilloscope was described briefly in the last chapter. Essentially it is a device which can give a reasonably accurate picture of the signal waveform at any point in a circuit. Oscilloscopes of many different types are available, and the selection of the ideal oscilloscope for a particular application can be quite an involved procedure.[1]   For ordinary testing purposes, however, a general-purpose, portable oscilloscope with a maximum bandwidth of about

[1] See *Fundamentals of selecting and using oscilloscopes*, Tektronix, Inc., Beaverton, Oreg.

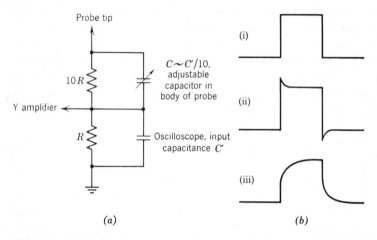

Fig. 10.7   (a) Circuit of a compensated attenuator probe for an oscilloscope; (b) oscilloscope waveforms with a square-wave input: (i) correctly compensated for C', (ii) C too large, overcompensated, (iii) C too small, undercompensated.

10 Mc/sec and a maximum sensitivity (usually at much-reduced bandwidth) of about 1 mV/cm, will meet the demands of most research laboratories.   If necessary, extra versatility can be obtained by purchasing an instrument with separate, plug-in amplifiers and time bases.   For fast nonsinusoidal signals it is usually essential to use a compensated attenuator probe, for which the basic circuit is illustrated in Fig. 10.7a, in order to avoid distortion of the input signal.   The effects of over- and undercompensation are shown in Fig. 10.7b.   Probes of all degrees of complexity are available, with various attachments such as crocodile clips, banana plugs, and spade terminals for connecting the probe to the signal source.   For work at audio frequencies the simplest type of probe—essentially a terminal on the end of a piece of shielded cable—is usually quite satisfactory.   For more sophisticated measurements it may be necessary to use a probe with a built-in cathode follower at the probe tip, or with an extra layer of shielding between the signal wire and the outer, earthed shield, the extra shield being driven by a cathode follower so that its potential follows that of the signal lead.   This means that the signal lead is always surrounded by a shield at the same potential as itself, and so a fast signal is not integrated by the

stray capacitance which is normally present between the central wire and the earthed shield.

Often one part of an instrument can function as a signal generator for another part during testing or trouble-shooting, and an external signal source is not required. Thus in a photometer which uses a chopped-light source the output from the light detector should give a signal which is suitable for observing the response of subsequent amplifier stages, unless there is something seriously wrong with the optics or with the detector itself. Failing this, however, there are innumerable types of signal generator available commercially, both in the form of pulse generators with outputs of controlled pulse height and shape, repetition rate, and mark-space ratio (ratio of the duration of a pulse to the time between pulses), and as sine-wave generators designed for various frequency ranges. The sine-wave generators normally also incorporate a Schmitt trigger so that the output can be changed from a sine wave to a square wave just by flicking a switch.

The multimeter, available commercially in many different models, is basically a moving-coil microammeter, typically of good quality and sensitivity of the order of 50 μA full scale. The incorporation of various series and shunt resistors and appropriate selector switches in the multimeter enables it to function as a multirange dc ammeter or voltmeter, the incorporation of a set of rectifying diodes enables it to function as an ac ammeter or voltmeter, and the incorporation of a battery or batteries, which can drive a measurable current through an external resistance, enables it to function as an ohmmeter. The multimeter is an exceedingly useful laboratory instrument whose only serious drawback is that it must not be used to measure the resistance of very low wattage resistors—for example, the multiturn potentiometers which form a part of many commercial automatic recording spectrophotometers—because the full-scale current of the meter is likely to be sufficient to burn out the resistor.

The vacuum tube voltmeter (VTVM), for which two different basic circuits are illustrated in Fig. 10.8, performs essentially the same functions as the multimeter, but with the advantages of greater sensitivity, especially in measuring very small currents, and higher input impedance. Whereas the input impedance of the multimeter is least when very small currents are being measured, that of the VTVM is greatest in the low-current range. The circuits of Fig. 10.8

can obviously be fitted out with shunts, voltage supplies, etc., in order to be capable of measuring resistance and ac and dc current and voltage.

When an apparatus is switched on for the first time, it is always necessary to apply some tests to see that it is working properly. If possible the switching should be done one section at a time—first the heater supplies for tubes, then the power supply, then the connections between the power supply and other units. At each stage the operator should be alert for burning smells and/or sizzling noises, on the assumption that anyone can make a mistake in wiring up a new circuit for the first time. Once everything has been switched on without incident, output voltage levels can be checked and the effect of an input signal can be observed. Often the results of the tests will be satisfactory and the equipment can be considered ready for immediate use.

Sometimes, however, when an apparatus is turned on for the first time, or even after it has been operating satisfactorily for months or years, the effect of operating the switch is either undesirable or undetectable, and trouble-shooting is called for. If the fault is only

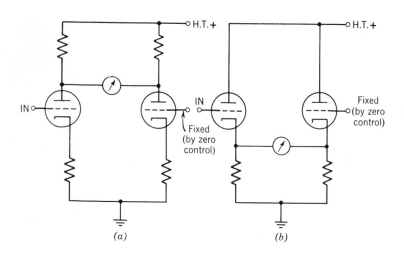

Fig. 10.8   Basic vacuum tube voltmeter circuits: (*a*) highly sensitive, not very stable, (*b*) very stable, moderately sensitive.

that the initial performance of the circuit is not as good as had been anticipated, this probably means that some approximations which were involved in the design procedure were too drastic, or that insufficient allowance was made for possible spreads in the characteristics of components; a satisfactory state of affairs should result from changing the values of a few components. If the breakdown is more serious, the trouble should first be isolated in one part of the instrument by checking the behavior of individual building blocks. Once the offending unit has been located, or even before this point is reached, the senses can be employed to detect burning smells, unusual frying noises, visible sparks or broken connections (fuses should have been checked first), and cold (i.e., unlit) vacuum tubes. The next step is to measure the internal voltage levels at tube anodes or at the collectors of transistors, between the ends of resistors, and so on, and to endeavour to trace an input signal through the circuit until a blockage is found. When the malfunction has been located in a single-circuit stage—amplifier, trigger circuit, feedback loop, etc.—individual components in this stage can be checked either by substitution or by *in situ* measurements. If the trouble is located in an extensive feedback loop, it is usually possible to pin it down more precisely by observing the behavior of the circuit with the loop broken at one point, e.g., after the removal of a tube. There are a few troubles which may not be picked up immediately by this sort of procedure—for example, breakdowns caused by unsuspected inverse voltage transients in circuits containing silicon rectifiers—and to discover the roots of these it may be necessary to exercise the imagination, spend some time in the library, or consult an expert in the field. There is a great deal of satisfaction to be derived from getting to the bottom of one of these problems, even if it does subtract from time spent in more productive pursuits. However, it turns out that in practice such problems are exceedingly rare, and the simple procedures just described will put an end to almost any trouble. Two other practical points should be mentioned in this connection. The first is that accumulated dust can cause intermittent failure or excessive noise in a circuit, and a source of compressed air for blowing dust out of the wiring is a useful addition to the list of test equipment. Sometimes it helps simply to loosen a tube in its socket, and then push it home again, if a film of dust or corrosion has caused a bad contact to form. The second point is that "dry" soldered joints are usually apparent as soon as they are made, but poor joints can also develop at any time as a result of corrosion by the laboratory atmosphere, use of an excessively violent soldering flux, or fatigue fracture in the joint.   Defective joints can usually be located by observing the effect on the signal of a solid pull on the insulation of individual connecting leads.   A bad joint can be either temporarily improved or permanently devastated by this means, and in either case the result is readily apparent.

10c   SOME COMPLETE ELECTRONIC INSTRUMENTS

The first instrument to be considered is the simple dc photometer whose exterior view was given in Fig. 10.2.   A block diagram of this instrument is given in Fig. 10.9.   The photometer uses a 1P21, 1P28, or similar type of photomultiplier, in combination with optical filters to isolate the desired spectral region.   The heart of the instrument is a vacuum tube voltmeter, similar to that of Fig. 10.8*b*, which responds to the voltage developed by the photocurrent across the grid resistor of one 12AT7 triode section.   As shown in Fig. 10.10, the sensitivity

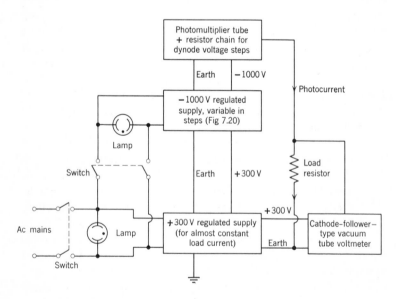

Fig. 10.9   Block diagram of the dc photometer of Fig. 10.2.

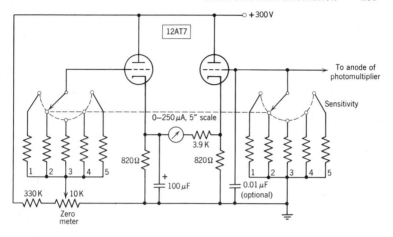

Fig. 10.10 Vacuum tube voltmeter section of dc photometer. Resistor between grid and earth at different sensitivity settings: (1) 220 K, (2) 1.0 M, (3) 4.7 M, (4) 22 M, (5) 100 M.

is varied by changing the size of the grid resistor, and the effect of any grid current is largely canceled by switching grid resistors in both sections of the 12AT7 simultaneously. The photomultiplier is driven from the power supply of Fig. 7.20, and the 300 V supply, which operates with an almost constant load, is shown in Fig. 10.11.

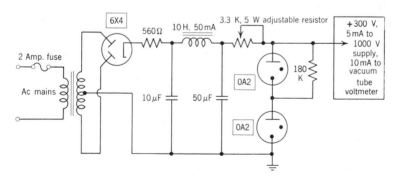

Fig. 10.11 300 V regulated supply for dc photometer. The adjustable resistor is fixed so that 15 mA flows through the OA2 tubes. The transformer supplies 350, 0, −350 V rms, and 6.3 V at 1 A for the 6X4 and 12AT7 filaments.

The 100 μF capacitor which is inserted in parallel with the cathode resistor of the left-hand 12AT7 section is intended to increase the time constant of the meter.

The sensitivity of the photometer just described is limited by the lack of voltage amplification, other than what occurs internally in the photomultiplier tube, and ultimately by flicker noise in the triode sections and shot noise in the photomultiplier dark current. Shot noise in the grid current of the two triodes will also be significant if the grid resistors are made very large, unless special efforts are made to reduce the grid current. By using a "light chopper" and ac amplification, it is possible to eliminate practically all the flicker noise, so that the main remaining limitation is shot noise in the dark current, which can be greatly reduced by refrigerating the photomultiplier.

A block diagram of a very sensitive photometer, which uses a 600 cycles/sec chopper followed by ac amplification and a phase-sensitive detector, is given in Fig. 10.12. The only part of this instrument which has not been described in some earlier chapter is the combination amplifier, variable phase shift, and Schmitt trigger which converts the 600 cycle reference signal from the vacuum photocell into a gating signal for the phase-sensitive detector. This portion of the circuit is given in Fig. 10.13. The correct phase relationship between the light signal and the square-wave gating signal is established initially with the aid of an oscilloscope, with the probe applied to the cathode of one of the lower 12AT7 sections of Fig. 6.15, and adjusted thereafter by selecting the phase setting which gives a maximum meter reading. The meter response can usefully be slowed down by putting it in parallel with a large capacitor, 100 μF, for example, in series with a 1000 ohm resistor. This circuitry could also be used with other types of photodetector—for example, a lead sulfide photoconductor or Golay detector,[2] but it would probably be necessary to use a preamplifier to increase the initial signal level by a factor of 10^2 or 10^3, and to cut down the chopping frequency to about 100 cycles/sec. In order to obtain a further improvement in sensitivity at very low light levels, it is necessary to resort to pulse techniques, i.e., to count the pulses produced by individual photons arriving at the cathode of a photomultiplier. A block diagram of such an instrument is given in Fig. 10.14.

A somewhat different type of instrument is the ac conductance

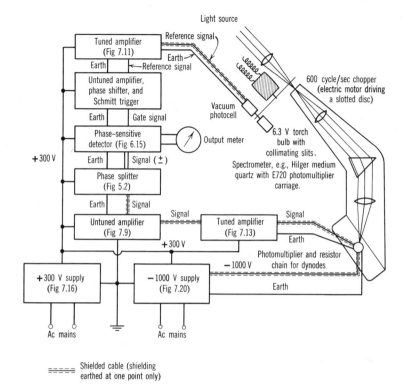

Fig. 10.12 Block diagram of a spectrophotometer using a chopped light source. Output meter, 0–50 μA, with various series resistors (1 K, 10 K, 100 K) and a suitable *RC* damping network.

bridge which is illustrated in Fig. 10.15. This instrument is intended primarily for student use as a device for measuring electrolytic conductance, in which role it illustrates among other things the use of a *Wagner earth* to reduce the effects of stray capacitance (see footnote 2, page 130). If desired, the Wien bridge capacitors in the oscillator can be varied by means of a selector switch, so that the output frequency of the oscillator is varied over the range from about 1 to 10 kc. The electrodes which are inserted into the

[2] See T. S. Moss, "Modern infrared detectors," in *Advances in spectroscopy*, H. W. Thompson ed., Volume I. New York: Interscience Publishers, 1959.

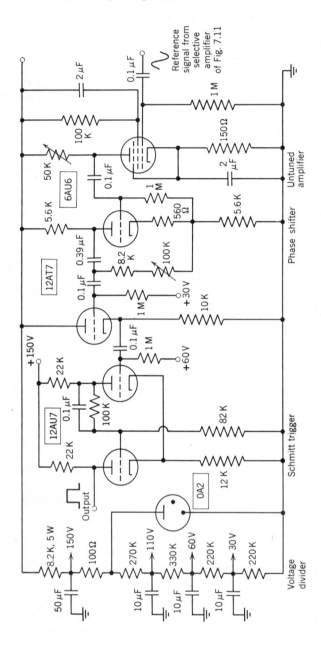

Fig. 10.13   Circuit to produce the gating signal for the phase-sensitive detector of Fig. 6.15.   The load resistor of the 6AU6 is adjusted to give a symmetrical square wave as the final output of the circuit.

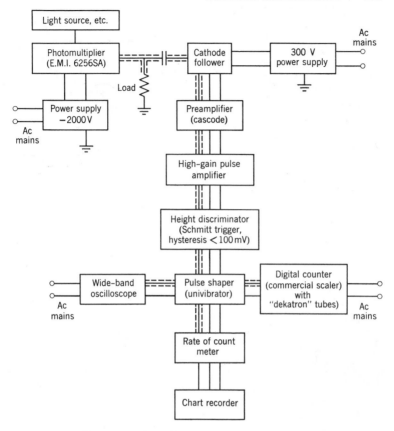

Fig. 10.14   Block diagram of a quantum counter.

electrolyte should preferably be coated with platinum black in order to simplify the problem of obtaining a capacitance balance, and for best results the actual resistance of the conductance cell should be between 1000 and 100,000 ohms.

Finally, as an example of how a complex instrument results from the connecting together of a number of relatively simple building blocks, we consider a conventional magnetic-deflection mass spectrometer. A block diagram of a mass spectrometer is given in Fig. 10.16. In designing an instrument with as many interacting parts as this contains, it is necessary to aim for extreme reliability of each subunit within the limits set by the required performance of the

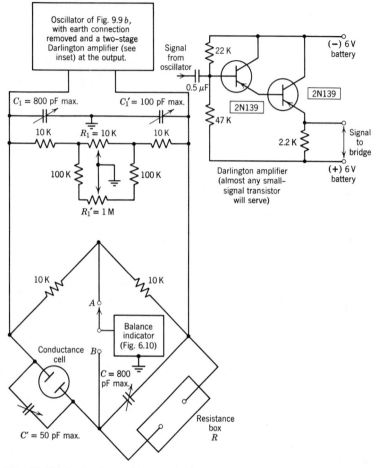

Fig. 10.15 Student's conductance bridge with Wagner earthing device. In use the balance indicator is switched to *A* and then $R_1, R_1', C_1,$ and C_1' are adjusted to give a minimum out-of-balance signal. The indicator is then switched to *B*, and a new balance is obtained by varying *R*, *C*, and *C'*. The detector is then switched back to *A*, and the whole process is repeated as often as necessary to secure a final balance. In practice, it may sometimes be necessary to connect an additional, external capacitor in parallel with the conductance cell or resistance box.

complete machine. For this reason it is best to pay a little more for a well-tried commercial product when the function to be carried out is a critical one—for example, the vibrating-reed electrometer of Fig. 10.16 (see Fig. 5.16, page 116) or to use a proven circuit taken from

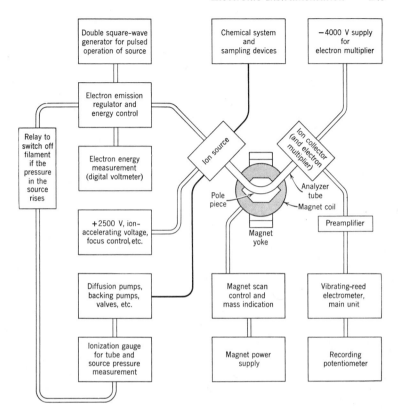

Fig. 10.16   Block diagram of a conventional magnetic scanning mass spectrometer. The ac line voltage regulator, main switch panel, and most of the protective relay system are not shown. The electron multiplier is optional.

the literature for a unit which is less difficult to build but whose proper performance is vital to the instrument as a whole—for example, the high-voltage power supply of Fig. 10.16 (see footnote 7, page 161). Apart from the major units, however, any complex instrument contains a number of peripheral items which it is useful to be able to design and build from scratch. For the mass spectrometer such an item would be the double square-wave generator of Fig. 10.17, which is designed to take the output from a commercial wide-range oscillator (e.g., Hewlett-Packard model 200S) and convert it into two out-of-phase square waves of amplitude 20 V peak to peak. The two square waves are required during pulse operation of the ion

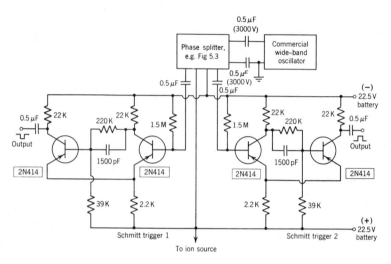

Fig. 10.17   Double square-wave generator.

source; one turns off the electron gun while the other repels ions from the ion chamber.   During the other half of the cycle, with the electron gun turned on, ions are formed, and ion-molecule reactions can take place in an essentially field-free region.

REFERENCES

1.   H. V. Malmstadt, C. G. Enke, and E. C. Toren, *Electronics for scientists.* New York: W. A. Benjamin, 1963.   (Many highly instructive experiments are described at the ends of the chapters.)

2.   H. A. Romanowitz, *Fundamentals of semiconductor and tube electronics.* New York: John Wiley & Sons, Inc., 1962.   (This book is supplemented by a laboratory manual and an instructor's manual.)

3.   W. C. Elmore and M. Sands, *Electronics.*   New York: McGraw-Hill Book Company, 1949, Chapter 1.

4.   E. J. Bair, *Introduction to chemical instrumentation.*   New York: McGraw-Hill Book Company, 1962, Chapters 2, 4, 8, and 9.

5.   For an extensive list of references relevant to this and to most previous chapters, see *GE transistor manual*, Syracuse, N.Y.: General Electric Company.   Sixth Edition, 1962, p. 379.

Appendix *1*

Elementary Matrix Algebra

··

Reference: Margenau and Murphy, *The mathematics of physics and chemistry.* New York: D. Van Nostrand, Second Edition, 1956, Chapter 10.

1. A general matrix is

$$(A) = \begin{vmatrix} a_{11} & a_{12} & a_{13} & \cdots & a_{1m} \\ a_{21} & a_{22} & a_{23} & \cdots & a_{2m} \\ \cdot & \cdot & \cdot & \cdot & \cdot \\ a_{n1} & a_{n2} & a_{n3} & \cdots & a_{nm} \end{vmatrix}$$

2. A *square* matrix has $m = n$.

3. Two matrices (A) and (B) are equal if $a_{ij} = b_{ij}$ for all i, j. (A) and (B) must have the same numbers of rows and columns.

4. The sum (C) of two matrices (A) and (B) is a matrix such that

$$c_{ij} = a_{ij} + b_{ij} \qquad \text{for all } i, j.$$

(A) and (B) must have the same numbers of rows and columns. Similarly, the difference (D) is a matrix such that

$$d_{ij} = a_{ij} - b_{ij} \qquad \text{for all } i, j.$$

5. A null matrix has $a_{ij} = 0$ for all i, j.

6. A diagonal matrix has $a_{ij} = 0$ for all $i \neq j$.

7. A unit matrix has $a_{ij} = 1$, for $i = j$, and $a_{ij} = 0$ for $i \neq j$, i.e.,

$$a_{ij} = \delta_{ij}$$

8.   The product (C) of two matrices (A) and (B) is a matrix such that

$$c_{ij} = \sum_k a_{ik}b_{kj}$$

where the number of columns in (A) must equal the number of rows in (B).

9.   The associative and distributive laws of multiplication hold, but not the commutative law, i.e.,

$$(A)(BC) = (A)(B)(C)$$

and

$$(A)(B + C) = (A)(B) + (A)(C)$$

but

$$(A)(B) \neq (B)(A)$$

10.   A square matrix (A) has a reciprocal $(A)^{-1}$ which is given by $(\hat{A})/|A|$, where $|A|$ is the determinant of (A), i.e.,

$$|A| = \begin{vmatrix} a_{11} & a_{12} & a_{13} & \cdots & a_{1n} \\ a_{21} & a_{22} & a_{23} & \cdots & a_{2n} \\ \cdot & \cdot & \cdot & \cdot & \cdot \\ a_{n1} & a_{n2} & a_{n3} & \cdots & a_{nn} \end{vmatrix}$$

and $(\hat{A})$ is a matrix whose elements $\hat{a}_{ij}$ are the cofactors of the transposed elements a_{ji} in this determinant.   (The cofactor of a_{ji} is the determinant which results from crossing out row j and column i in the determinant $|A|$.)

11.   The set of n linear equations

$$y_1 = a_{11}x_1 + a_{12}x_2 + \cdots a_{1n}x_n$$
$$y_2 = a_{21}x_1 + a_{22}x_2 + \cdots a_{2n}x_n$$
$$\cdot \quad \cdot \quad \cdot \quad \cdot \quad \cdot \quad \cdot \quad \cdot \quad \cdot \quad \cdot$$
$$y_n = a_{n1}x_1 + a_{n2}x_2 + \cdots a_{nn}x_n$$

can be written in the form

$$\begin{pmatrix} y_1 \\ y_2 \\ \cdots \\ y_n \end{pmatrix} = \begin{pmatrix} a_{11} & a_{12} & a_{13} & \cdots & a_{1n} \\ a_{21} & a_{22} & a_{23} & \cdots & a_{2n} \\ \cdot & \cdot & \cdot & \cdot & \cdot \\ a_{n1} & a_{n2} & a_{n3} & \cdots & a_{nn} \end{pmatrix} \begin{pmatrix} x_1 \\ x_2 \\ \cdots \\ x_n \end{pmatrix}$$

or simply

$$(Y) = (A)(X)$$

12. If $\quad (Y) = (A)(X)$

as above, then

$$(X) = (A)^{-1}(Y)$$

13. If $\quad (Y) = (A)(X)$

and $\quad (Z) = (B)(Y)$

then $\quad (Z) = (C)(X)$

where $\quad (C) = (B)(A)$

14. If $\quad (Y) = (A)(X)$

and $\quad (Z) = (B)(X)$

then $\quad (Y) + (Z) = (C)(X)$

where $\quad (C) = (A) + (B)$

Appendix *2*

Transistor Hybrid Parameters

It sometimes happens, for example, when very large values of load resistance are used with a common-emitter configuration, that the simple methods given in Chapter 4 for calculating the performance of transistor amplifier stages are not sufficiently accurate. In this situation more accurate results can generally be derived with the aid of the so-called hybrid (*h*) parameters. Furthermore, as control over the production spreads of transistor parameters improves, so will the greater precision which the hybrid parameters provide become meaningful enough to warrant their use in many more situations. A further point is that most manufacturers now give the characteristics of their products in terms of the hybrid parameters (as well as in any other system to which they may have become attached—see Appendix 3), so that the hybrid parameters constitute a kind of lingua franca for this field.

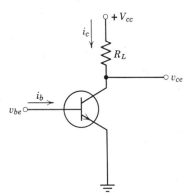

For a common-emitter stage we can write in general:

$$dv_{be} = \left(\frac{\partial v_{be}}{\partial i_b}\right)_{di_b} + \left(\frac{\partial v_{be}}{\partial v_{ce}}\right)_{dv_{ce}}$$

$$di_c = \left(\frac{\partial i_c}{\partial i_b}\right)_{di_b} + \left(\frac{\partial i_c}{\partial v_{ce}}\right)_{dv_{ce}}$$

In terms of *h* parameters these equations become

$$dv_{be} = h_{ie}\, di_b + h_{re}\, dv_{ce}$$
$$di_c = h_{fe}\, di_b + h_{oe}\, dv_{ce}$$

251

where h_{ie} is read as "h input emitter," h_{re} as "h reverse emitter," h_{fe} as "h forward emitter," and h_{oe} as "h output emitter."   If we now write

$$dv_{ce} = -R_L \, di_c$$

we can eliminate di_b and di_c from the last pair of equations, with the result that

$$\frac{dv_{ce}}{dv_{be}} = -\frac{h_{fe}R_L}{h_{ie} + R_L} \, [h_{ie}h_{oe} - h_{fe}h_{re}]$$

This expression gives the gain of the amplifier stage when it is driven by a signal source of zero output impedance.   The term within square brackets was neglected in Chapter 4.

For a common-base stage we can similarly write

$$dv_{eb} = h_{ib} \, di_e + h_{rb} \, dv_{cb}$$
$$di_c = h_{fb} \, di_e + h_{ob} \, dv_{cb}$$

and

$$dv_{cb} = -R_L \, di_c$$

so that

$$\frac{dv_{cb}}{dv_{eb}} = -\frac{h_{fb}R_L}{h_{ib} + R_L} \, [h_{ib}h_{ob} + f_{fb}h_{rb}]$$

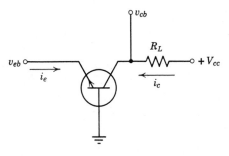

For a common-collector (emitter follower) stage we must have

$$dv_{bc} = h_{ic} \, di_b + h_{rc} \, dv_{ec}$$
$$di_e = h_{fc} \, di_b + h_{oc} \, dv_{ec}$$

In this case we have again

$$dv_{ec} = -R_L \, di_e$$

and so the voltage gain becomes

$$\frac{dv_{ec}}{dv_{bc}} = -\frac{h_{fc}R_L}{h_{ic} + R_L} \, [h_{ic}h_{oc} - h_{fc}h_{rc}]$$

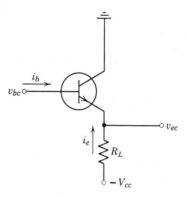

The table below shows how the various hybrid parameters are related to the parameters which were used in Chapter 4.

Conversion Table

Common Emitter	Common Base	Common Collector
$h_{ie} = r_{be}$	$h_{ib} = -r_e$	$h_{ic} = r_{be}$
$\quad = r_b + (1 + \beta)r_e$	$h_{rb} = \mu$	$h_{rc} = 1$
$h_{re} = \mu$	$h_{fb} = -\alpha$	$h_{fc} = -(\beta + 1)$
$h_{fe} = \beta$	$h_{ob} = 1/r_{cb}$	$h_{oc} = -1/r_c$
$h_{oe} = 1/r_c$	$\quad = 1/r_c - \beta\mu/r_{be}$	

Note: In a number of places in this table we have neglected μ in comparison with unity.

Appendix 3

Symbols and Abbreviations

··

Manufacturers and authors in different countries employ a variety of symbols for the parameters which describe the behavior of electronic circuits and components.   Thus E_b or V_a may be preferred for the plate voltage of a tube, α', β, or h_{fe} for the small-signal current gain of a transistor, and so on.   To help the reader avoid confusion a comparison list, showing corresponding symbols used by Mullard (British), RCA (American), Philips (European), and the present author (nonaligned), is given as the first part of this appendix. Following this list is a short glossary which contains some other common symbols and abbreviations.   These lists are not intended to be exhaustive but should contain what is essential for most purposes.

EQUIVALENT SYMBOLS

Tube parameter	Mullard	Philips	RCA	This book
Amplification factor	μ	μ	μ	μ
Anode current[1]	I_a	I_a	I_b	i_a
Anode dissipation	p_a	W_a	P_p	P_a
Anode load resistance	R_a	R_a	R_L	R_L
Anode resistance (internal)	r_a	R_i	r_p	ρ
Anode supply voltage[1]	$V_{a(b)}$	V_{ba}	E_{bb}	HT +, V_{supply}
Anode (plate) voltage[1]	V_a	V_a	E_b	v_a
Anode voltage peak	$V_{a(pk)}$	V_{ap}	E_{bm}	—

Filament (heater) current	I_f, I_h	I_f	I_f	i_h
Filament (heater) voltage	V_f, V_h	V_f	E_f	v_h
Grid current[1]	I_g	I_g	I_c	i_g
Grid voltage[1]	V_g	V_g	E_c	v_g
Mutual conductance (trans-conductance	g_m	S	g_m	g_m

Transistor parameter	Mullard	Philips	RCA	This book
Collector dissipation	P_c	P_c	P_c	P_c
Collector-emitter voltage	V_{CE}	V_{CE}	V_{CE}	v_{ce}
Collector supply voltage	V_{CC}	V_{CC}	E_{CC}	V_{cc}
Cutoff frequency for α	f_α	$f_{\alpha b}$	f_{hfb}	f_α
Cutoff frequency for β	$f_{\alpha'}$	$f_{\alpha e}$	f_{hfe}	f_β
Emitter current	I_E	I_E	I_E	i_e
Forward current transfer ratio (common base)	α	α_{fb}	α, h_{fb}	α
Forward current transfer ratio (common emitter)	α'	α_{fe}	β, h_{fe}	β
Internal base resistance	r_b	r_b	r_b	r_b
Internal base-emitter resistance[2]	$r_{b'e}$	h_{ie}	h_{ie}	r_{be}
Internal emitter resistance	r_e	r_e	r_e	r_e
Internal collector resistance[3] (common base)	r_c	$1/h_{ob}$	$1/h_{ob}$	r_{cb}
Internal collector resistance (common emitter)	$r_{c'}$	$1/h_{oe}$	$1/h_{oe}$	r_c
Large-signal current gain	$\bar{\alpha}'$	α_{FE}	h_{FE}	β
Load resistance	R_L	R_L	R_L	R_L
Noise figure	F	F	NF	F
Reverse voltage transfer ratio (common base)	μ	h_{rb}	h_{rb}	μ
Small-signal current gain	α'	α_{fe}	β, h_{fe}	β
Thermal resistance (°C/watt)	θ	K	K	θ

---

[1] Sometimes capital or small letters are used indiscriminately for E, V, and I; sometimes the difference is significant. If in doubt, consult the manufacturer's manual.

[2] $r_{be} = r_b + (1 + \beta)r_e$.

[3] $r_{cb} = r_c/(1 - r_c\beta\mu/r_{be})$.

COMMON ABBREVIATIONS

Ambient temperature	T_{amb}
Amplitude modulation	am
Audiofrequency	af
Automatic gain control	agc
Bandwidth	B
Breakdown voltage (emitter or base circuit open)	BV_{CBO}, BV_{CEO}; $V_{(BR)CBO}$, $V_{(BR)CEO}$
Cutoff frequency, $\|h_{fe}\| = 1$	f_1
Cycles per second	cps, Hz (short for Hertz)
Decibel	db
Extra-high tension (i.e., kilovolts)	EHT
Femto- (prefix, $=10^{-15}$)	f-
Field-effect transistor	FET
Frequency modulation	fm
Gain-bandwidth product (of a high-frequency transistor)	f_T
Giga- (prefix, $=10^{+9}$)	G-
High frequency	hf
High tension (i.e., about 300 V)	HT
Input admittance	Y_i, g_i
Intermediate frequency	if
Internally connected (pins on a tube)	i.c.
Joint Electron Device Engineering Council	JEDEC
Junction temperature	T_j
Kilo- (prefix, $=10^{+3}$)	k-
Mega- (prefix, $=10^{+6}$)	M-
Micro- (prefix, $=10^{-6}$)	μ-
Milli (prefix, $=10^{-3}$)	m-
Nano- (prefix, $=10^{-9}$)	n-
Negative temperature coefficient	NTC
Not connected (pins on a tube)	NC
Peak inverse voltage (of diode)	PIV
Pico- (prefix, $=10^{-12}$)	p-, $\mu\mu$-
Radiofrequency	rf
Root mean square	rms

Silicon controlled rectifier	SCR
Storage temperature	T_s
Tera- (prefix, $= 10^{+12}$)	T-
Ultra-high frequency	uhf
Vacuum-tube voltmeter	VTVM
Very high frequency	vhf
Working voltage (of a capacitor)	VW
Zener voltage	V_z

Appendix *4* Circuit Symbols

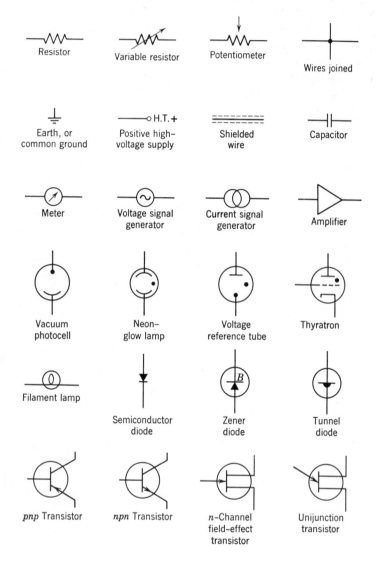

Resistor

Variable resistor

Potentiometer

Wires joined

Earth, or
common ground

Positive high-
voltage supply

Shielded
wire

Capacitor

Meter

Voltage signal
generator

Current signal
generator

Amplifier

Vacuum
photocell

Neon-
glow lamp

Voltage
reference tube

Thyratron

Filament lamp

Semiconductor
diode

Zener
diode

Tunnel
diode

pnp Transistor

npn Transistor

n-Channel
field-effect
transistor

Unijunction
transistor

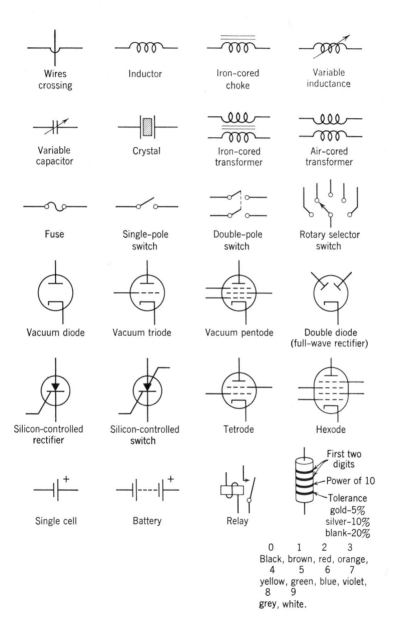

Wires crossing Inductor Iron-cored choke Variable inductance

Variable capacitor Crystal Iron-cored transformer Air-cored transformer

Fuse Single-pole switch Double-pole switch Rotary selector switch

Vacuum diode Vacuum triode Vacuum pentode Double diode (full-wave rectifier)

Silicon-controlled rectifier Silicon-controlled switch Tetrode Hexode

Single cell Battery Relay

First two digits
Power of 10
Tolerance
gold–5%
silver–10%
blank–20%

0   1   2   3
Black, brown, red, orange,
4   5   6   7
yellow, green, blue, violet,
8   9
grey, white.

Index

DATE DUE